"In a straightforward, easy-to-read, and profound way, the 1
biblical principles necessary for high achievement, personal happiness, and business success.

— WILLARD THEISSEN, FOUNDER AND HOST,

It's a New Day, CHRISTIAN TELEVISION SHOW, NOW TV, CANADA

"A riveting, timeless, literary work. Biblically-sound, it should be required reading for every
Christian. This book is vital for discovering your God-given purpose and achieving unparalleled
success."

— RICARDO M. MARTIN, FOUNDER AND PUBLISHER,

CHRISTIAN COVENANT NEWSPAPERS, MICHIGAN

"Revolutionary, practical and powerful wisdom to get into God's perfect will for your life. It
challenges people of every age and all walks of life to step into their personal greatness and realize their God-given potential."

— BISHOP GEORGE L. DAVIS, SENIOR PASTOR,

FAITH CHRISTIAN CENTER, FLORIDA

"Bound to be a classic — *How to Discover Your Purpose in 10 Days* brings a unique depth and
practicality to the teaching on purpose. Engaging, profound, and filled with rich, vivid examples, the Eagans give insight from their personal life experiences in discovering and operating
successfully in God's perfect will."

— PASTORS BEN & JEWEL TANKARD, SENIOR PASTORS AND FOUNDERS,

DESTINY CENTER, TENNESSEE

"Using pragmatic examples, the Eagans masterfully minister the Word of God in answering one of
life's most fundamental and perplexing questions: 'What on earth am I here for?' Essential for
everyone who wants to discover God's plan for their lives!"

— AL HOLLINGSWORTH, PRESIDENT AND CEO,

ALDELANO PACKAGING CORPORATION, CALIFORNIA

"Truly a work of God! This anointed, brilliant, and easy-to-understand book will change your
life. After the Eagans taught these principles to my staff, our office was transformed. Not only
did people develop a greater appreciation and love for their jobs, our profitability soared and
our productivity went to greater heights!"

— DR. BARRY RUSSELL, PRESIDENT AND CEO,

LOFTANN ENTERPRISES, LIMITED, NASSAU, BAHAMAS

How to Discover Your

Purpose

in 10 Days

Self-Assessment

Workbook

Other Books Authored by the Eagans Include:

Dominating Business
How to Prosper on Your Job

Anointed for Work
Using the Tools from Sunday to Succeed on Monday

How to Determine Your Motivational Gift
Learn How God Wired You

Dominating Money
Personal Financial Intelligence

The Character of Success
26 Characteristics of Highly Successful People

The Word @ Work, Volumes I & II
Scriptures for the Workplace

How to Discover Your Purpose in 10 Days
God's Path to a Full and Satisfied Life

How to Discover Your Purpose in 10 Days
Prayers and Daily Journal

Upcoming Books Include:

Godly Leadership in the Workplace

The Road to the Wealthy Place
Dominating Money in Business

Terminating Conflict
God's Solutions to Resolving Conflict Permanently

All titles are available on-line at www.eaganbooks.com.
Also available: CDs and DVDs.
For more information, E-mail us at info@eaganbooks.com
or call 1-877-EAGANS1 (324-2671).

HOW TO DISCOVER YOUR PURPOSE *in* 10 DAYS SELF-ASSESSMENT WORKBOOK

DR. J. VICTOR AND
CATHERINE B. EAGAN

WORKPLACE
WISDOM

WORKPLACE
WISDOM

SOUTHFIELD, MICHIGAN 48076 USA

How to Discover Your Purpose in 10 Days Self-Assessment Workbook
Copyright © 2004 by Dr. J. Victor and Catherine B. Eagan.

Workplace Wisdom Publishing, LLC.,
17600 W. 12 Mile Road, Suite 1, Southfield, Michigan 48076.
www.workplacewisdompublishing.com • www.eaganbooks.com • 1-877-EAGANS1 (324-2671)

Publisher's Cataloging-in-Publication Data
(Prepared by The Donohue Group, Inc.)

Eagan, J. Victor.
    How to discover your purpose : self-assessment workbook / J. Victor
and Catherine B. Eagan.
        p. ; cm.
        ISBN: 1-932477-02-0
1. Self-actualization (Psychology)--Problems, exercises, etc. 2.
Spiritual life. I. Eagan, Catherine B. II. Title.

BF637.S4 E142 2004
158.1   2004110722

Cover Design by Brand Navigation — Bill Chiaravalle, Terra Petersen. www.brandnavigation.com
Interior Design by Pneuma Books, LLC. www.pneumabooks.com

Printed in the United States of America.

09 08 07 06 05   10 9 8 7 6 5 4 3 2 1

DEDICATION

This book is dedicated to Mrs. Louise Eagan and Mrs. Adele Helen Cartey,
our mothers, who understood the gifts God created each of us to be.
While raising us, they overcame many obstacles and made sacrifices
to ensure that we would reach our God-given potential.
They nurtured, encouraged, and allowed us to flow in our purpose
to the glory of God; and for that, we are eternally grateful.

Also, to every person who is in search of purpose
and to those who are in search of their God-given greatness
to the glory of God.

Table of Contents

Foreword

*T*he greatest tragedy in life is not death, but life without a purpose. It is more tragic to be alive and not know why than to be dead and not know life. Without purpose life has no meaning and existence has no reason, therefore, the greatest discovery in life is the discovery of personal purpose and destiny. The most important thing in life is the pursuit and fulfillment of that purpose. Therefore, knowledge and understanding of the processes that lead to its fulfillment are critical and must be the concern of every individual.

There is no greater discovery than the discovery of personal purpose. The discovery of purpose is the heart of life and the revelation that gives life meaning and value. Without purpose life has no relevance and time has no reason. What is purpose? Purpose is defined as the original reason for the creation of a thing — the original intent for the existence of a thing. In essence, purpose is why a product was created. Purpose is the end for which the means exists. Thus, purpose is the only true source of meaning and fulfillment in life.

For many years now I have taught, counseled, and researched the subject of purpose and its meaning to millions of people; and I am convinced that until an individual discovers a sense of purpose and destiny in their lives, living is nothing but an aimless experiment in daily frustration. I also contend that most anti-social behavior, violent crime, and substance abuse is a direct result of the absence of a sense of purpose in the lives of members of our societies. The discovery of a sense of purpose and destiny produces a spirit of responsibility, discipline, and order in life.

It is said that the poorest man in the world is the man without a dream. If this is true, then the most frustrated man in the world is the man with a dream that never becomes a reality. Knowing the end of a journey but not knowing the way to get there is an exercise in disillusionment. We all need help in getting to the end of our dream and arriving at our destiny. In essence we need a plan, a life map.

Dr. Victor and Catherine Eagan in *How to Discover Your Purpose in 10 Days* provide the missing link to knowing your dream and its fulfillment. The content of this work is imperative for the individual who wants to achieve his or her ultimate goals in life. Victor and Catherine with their simple, yet profound approach to this most important subject provide practical steps and easy-to-understand principles as an action plan to identify, discover, understand, explore, and take you on a journey to find and fulfill your purpose. The authors leap over complicated theoretical and philosophical jargon to present user-friendly concepts anyone can apply. Their progressive line-upon-line delivery of action-oriented directions for the reader is like a manual for life.

How to Discover Your Purpose in 10 Days is a natural and excellent companion book to my earlier published work, *In Pursuit of Purpose*, and provides the next step in the process of fulfilling your personal and corporate purpose.

I recommend the work highly and believe it will be the key to filling the gap between knowing your purpose and destiny and getting there. Everyone who desires to live a full life, maximize their potential, and make a lasting impact on their generation will find this book a necessary part of the process. Read each page and peel the wisdom from every paragraph. The wisdom contained in this book will take you leap years forward to your dream and save you many unnecessary mistakes and regrets through the process.

How to Discover Your Purpose in 10 Days will become a classic in the lives of thousands of purpose-driven people and a must for every library. Open these pages, read with an open mind, embrace the practical principles, and take action today. If you do, I'll see you at the end of your dream.

Dr. Victor and Catherine Eagan have been personal friends for many years, and I can attest to their passion and commitment to helping you and others

ADDITIONAL THOUGHTS

ADDITIONAL THOUGHTS

pursue their God-given assignment in life and fill the earth with their purpose. Their personal accomplishments and purpose-directed lives are prototypes of the principles in this book. The subject of purpose has been a critical part of my ministry for over thirty years, and I know that the Eagans are qualified to address this topic with much authority. I commend this work to you without reservation.

DR. MYLES MUNROE, CEO AND PRESIDENT
BFM GROUP OF COMPANIES

WORKPLACE
WISDOM

Preface

For over fifteen years we have traveled across the United States, Canada, and around the world teaching biblical principles in the areas of business and finance. In doing so, we discovered a great tragedy, namely that the vast majority of people do not know their purpose. Either that or they have hit a ceiling in the search for significance. Knowing one's purpose is fundamental to pleasing God and having a full life here on earth.

Our heart is to see people get into their purpose and fulfill their God-given destiny. We have encountered people from all walks of life — rich and poor, believers and unbelievers, workers and the unemployed — and among them we have observed a common thread which gave rise to our deep-felt passion. That thread was that an exceptional few understood their purpose. This provoked us to deep study, endless prayer, and revelation from God on the matter.

That desire led to an anointing from God to teach people *how* to get into their purpose and live the good life that He preordained before the foundation of the earth. Thousands have come to know their purpose through our teachings and have prospered in their families, relationships, workplaces, businesses, and finances. It is our greatest desire that you will be added to that number.

Both of us have been tremendously blessed by God. As children, we knew what we were called and assigned to do on earth. While our stories are individually different, there are common denominators — purpose known, obstacles overcome by God's grace, and fulfillment realized through operating in the perfect will of God for our lives.

We wrote *How to Discover Your Purpose in 10 Days* to empower every person to get into their purpose and to excel to such heights that God's glory might be seen on His children as they rule and reign with Him in this life. The gifts and calling of God are without repentance. God's gifts inside of you are inexhaustible.

How to Discover Your Purpose in 10 Days was written under a precious anointing from the Holy Spirit to help you seek God, learn your gifts, develop your talents, understand how He wired you, and fulfill your destiny.

We have prayed for you and we know that as you are faithful to read each day's lesson, pray, and complete the action plans using the *Self-Assessment*

Workbook and the *Prayers and Daily Journal,* God will show Himself and you will be blessed. (Jeremiah 29:11)

God is expecting to give you a great end,

The Eagans

Acknowledgments

WE WOULD LIKE TO THANK:
Our Heavenly Father, for anointing and calling us to our purpose
Each other, for always supporting, loving, and encouraging one another
Our parents, whose love, prayers, and guidance inspired us
Our spiritual parents, Bishop Keith A. Butler and Minister Deborah Butler
And other gifted people whose dedication helped us write this book:
Bill Gothard, Institute in Basic Life Principles
Marilyn Hickey, Marilyn Hickey Ministries
Don and Katie Fortune, Authors
Dr. Myles Munroe, Chairman,
International Third World Leaders Association
Starra Pollard, our Executive Assistant
Lauren Doyle-Davis, our Personal Assistant
Pneuma Books, LLC, our Interior Designers
Brand Navigation, LLC, our Graphic Artists

PURPOSE
INTRODUCTION

Introduction

Welcome to *How to Discover Your Purpose in 10 Days: God's Path to a Full and Satisfied Life.* This is a special edition of the purpose seminar that my wife and I have been teaching throughout the nation for the past decade. We are honored that God has given us the privilege of sharing fundamental principles for finding and fulfilling your purpose, and we are excited that you will be joining us on a 10-day journey to discovering God's plan for your life.

This system works. Read the teaching and complete the *action plans* and *self-assessments* that accompany each lesson. Use the *Prayers and Daily Journal* to write down your thoughts each day. We promise that if you diligently and prayerfully complete the 10-day process, God will begin to reveal to you His plans, desires, and purpose for your life.

There is nothing worse than wandering aimlessly in life, never reaching your full potential. God's best is for you to have success. This is possible when you walk in the fullness of what He has for you. God designed you to do great and mighty exploits on earth; and we pray that as you complete these 10 days you will begin to walk in the greatness that He preordained for you before the foundation of the world.

The material is life changing and it will be the same for you as it has been for countless others throughout the years. We are extremely excited for you! Our prayer is that God will reveal His specific purpose for your life and you will excel to the glory of God.

HOW TO USE THIS BOOK

How to Discover Your Purpose in 10 Days is designed to help you facilitate and identify your purpose. We as Christians are often told that God has a purpose for our lives; yet for many it is difficult to determine what that is. There are three types of people: those who do not know their God-given purpose; those who know their purpose, but are underdeveloped in it; and those who know their purpose, are developed, and maturing.

No matter what stage of life you may be in right now, this book is for you!

How to Discover Your Purpose in 10 Days is a step-by-step, simple, yet comprehensive way to identify who God made you to be. It's an exciting journey to once and for all discover the greatness within you that

God had in mind when He formed you in your mother's womb.

> Before I formed you in the womb I knew you; before you were born I sanctified you; I ordained you a prophet to the nations.
>
> JEREMIAH 1:5 (NKJV)

How to Discover Your Purpose in 10 Days is designed to propel you to new heights and teach you how to fulfill the perfect will of God for your life.

THE GOAL OF THE BOOK

The goal of *How to Discover Your Purpose in 10 Days* is to be a conduit in helping you understand your God-given, unique life assignment and unlock your personal greatness. At the same time, the book will help you feel good about yourself by helping you to understand yourself and others, including your family, your co-workers, children, boss, and friends.

The book is designed incrementally; and each day builds upon the other. To obtain the maximum results from the book it is strongly recommended that you undertake it day by day, prayerfully. With great excitement and anticipation we pray that after the 10 days have been completed, you will discover your purpose and begin to walk in God's best for your life.

ADDITIONAL THOUGHTS

THE STRUCTURE

How to Discover Your Purpose in 10 Days is designed so that each day takes you further along the pathway to discovering your God-given life purpose. As you prayerfully read and complete the associated exercises, you will begin to tap into the greatness within you.

Day 1: Discovering the Greatness Within

Day 1 marks the beginning of the exciting 10-day journey to your pathway to purpose. Day 1 reveals many of the awesome reasons why it is vitally important to identify and realize your God-given destiny.

Day 2: The Pathway to Discover Your Purpose — The Formative Years

In Day 2, you will discover how your purpose is intricately and progressively revealed to you by God. Even as a young child, your interests, natural talents, and abilities reflect the greatness God placed on the inside of you before birth. You were elaborately and intricately fashioned in the image of God Almighty and He formed you with a magnificent destiny in mind.

Day 3: Narrowing Your Focus — Young Adulthood

Day 3 focuses on the importance of determining your ruling passion and allowing it to govern your decisions on educational training, activities, and jobs that you undertake during young adulthood. God placed a ruling passion within you that reflects your innermost being. Uncovering your ruling passion is pivotal in discovering your God-given purpose.

Day 4: Obstacles on the Pathway to Purpose

Day 4 is the day of breakthrough! It reveals many of the obstacles that may arise along your pathway to purpose. There are countless reasons why you may get diverted, distracted, or thwarted from your pathway to purpose. Day 4 helps you locate yourself, make the necessary adjustments, and begin operating in your purpose.

Day 5: God's Unique Motivational Gifts — Introduction/Perceiver

In Day 5, the motivational gifts are introduced and the motivational gift of the Perceiver is discussed. God has called the Perceiver to intercede on the behalf of others and distinguish between right and wrong.

Day 6: God's Unique Motivational Gifts — Server/Teacher

In Day 6, the motivational gifts of Server and Teacher are revealed. God has called the Server to perform the practical needs of others, while the Teacher has been anointed by God to manage and disseminate information.

Day 7: God's Unique Motivational Gifts — Exhorter/Giver

In Day 7, the motivational gifts of Exhorter and Giver are uncovered. God has called the Exhorter to

ADDITIONAL THOUGHTS

ADDITIONAL THOUGHTS

encourage and build people up, while the Giver has been anointed by God to mobilize resources for the aid and benefit of others.

Day 8: God's Unique Motivational Gifts — Administrator/Compassion

In Day 8, the motivational gifts of Administrator and Compassion are outlined. God has called the Administrator to facilitate, administrate, and organize, while the Compassion gift is anointed by God to attend to and care for the emotional needs of others. Day 8 also answers the questions and challenges often faced in attempting to narrow down your motivational gift.

Day 9: Maturing in Your Purpose — The Adult Years

By Day 9, you should have begun to discover your God-given purpose. With this exciting revelation, you will learn how important it is to become more developed and mature in your purpose. It is God's desire that you dominate to His glory in your vocation. To do this, you must mature in your life work. Not only will you please God, you will also live a satisfied and fulfilled life.

Day 10: Fulfilling the Greatness Within

There is a great life work that the Lord is counting on you to fulfill. There is also an awesome destiny that God has prepared before the foundation of the world for you to realize. So, this power-packed series concludes on Day 10 centering on how to make your purpose a reality in your life.

Introduction

You were fearfully and wonderfully made by God and He placed greatness on the inside of you before you were born. You have been called of God to do great and mighty exploits on earth and Day 10 reveals steps that will empower and enable you to soar in your life purpose.

Invite God to Help You

We suggest that prior to beginning each day of purpose that you pray and invite God to help you get revelation, knowledge, and understanding concerning the important information you are about to receive.

> Wisdom is the principal thing; Therefore get wisdom. And in all your getting, get understanding.   PROVERBS 4:7 (NKJV)

We pray,

> That the God of our Lord Jesus Christ, the Father of glory, may give to you the spirit of wisdom and revelation in the knowledge of Him, the eyes of your understanding being enlightened; that you may know what is the hope of His calling, what are the riches of the glory of His inheritance in the saints, and what is the exceeding greatness of His power toward us who believe, according to the working of His mighty power.
>
> EPHESIANS 1:17-19 (NKJV)

Next, prepare your heart and mind in Christ Jesus.

Earnestly seek understanding about how He created you and the unique purpose He planned for you to fulfill on earth — your special assignment, your life purpose.

> But without faith it is impossible to please Him, for he who comes to God must believe that He is, and that He is a rewarder of those who diligently seek Him.
>
> HEBREWS 11:6 (NKJV)

When you see this icon, turn to the *Prayers and Daily Journal* as instructed for additional exercises and activities.

Then, read each day's material, listen to the teaching, and complete the action plans and self-assessments that correspond to each day. They are designed to help you focus, identify areas for change, and receive the maximum benefit from the book.

Journal each day in your *Prayers and Daily Journal* and be careful not to overlook the small bits of information. Remember, we are carefully working on a puzzle that God has masterfully designed — you. So don't let any of the pieces get lost.

Purpose each day to embrace who God made you to be. Don't begrudge your uniqueness or belittle your importance. You are a royal priesthood and your contribution is important to the establishment of God's kingdom on earth. Know that He is depending on you to fulfill your purpose.

> But you are a chosen generation, a royal priesthood, a holy nation, His own special people, that you may proclaim the praises of Him who called you out of darkness into His marvelous light.   1 PETER 2:9 (NKJV)

What is required of you is time, discipline, and commitment.

Lastly, be mindful that 10 days is a short period of time to resolve two of life's most fundamental and perplexing questions — Who am I? And what on earth am I here for? Our goal is to get you on the path to discovering your purpose. It can be the beginning of one of the best journeys of your Christian life.

Remember, *God* is expecting greatness from your life.

May the Lord richly bless you as you discover your purpose.

The Eagans

How to Discover Your Purpose *in* 10 Days Self-Assessment Workbook

It is impossible to do everything people want you to do. You have just enough time to do God's will. Purpose-driven living leads to a simpler lifestyle and saner schedule.

RICK WARREN

A difficult time can be more readily endured if we retain the conviction that our existence holds a purpose — a cause to pursue, a person to love, a goal to achieve.

JOHN MAXWELL

Outstanding people have one thing in common: an absolute sense of mission.

ZIG ZIGLAR

The masterpiece of man is to live to the purpose.

BENJAMIN FRANKLIN

Multitudes of people, drifting aimlessly to and fro without a set purpose, deny themselves such fulfillment of their capacities, and the satisfying happiness which attends it. They are not wicked, they are only shallow. They are not mean or vicious; they simply are empty — shake them and they would rattle like gourds. They lack range, depth, and conviction. Without purpose their lives ultimately wander into the morass of dissatisfaction. As we harness our abilities to a steady purpose and undertake the long pull toward its accomplishment, rich compensations reward us. A sense of purpose simplifies life and therefore concentrates our abilities; and concentration adds power.

KENNETH HILDEBRAND

Singleness of purpose is one of the chief essentials for success in life, no matter what may be one's aim.

JOHN D. ROCKEFELLER

There is one quality which one must possess to win, and that is definiteness of purpose, the knowledge of what one wants, and a burning desire to possess it.

NAPOLEON HILL

PURPOSE

DAY ONE

Day 1 marks the beginning of the exciting 10-day journey to your pathway to purpose. Day 1 reveals many of the awesome reasons why it is vitally important to identify and realize your God-given destiny. You will also learn about the hidden problems of never discovering and fulfilling your life purpose.

1

Discovering the Greatness Within

You have a specific God-given purpose which was preordained before birth. God made man to have a relationship with Him and He expects him to spend time with Him. By seeking the face of God, you can receive revelation from Him on the purpose for which you, individually, were created.

When God formed the world and everything within it, He had a specific purpose in mind for all of His creation. From the stars to the seas, everything was designed to fulfill a certain mission; including the most precious creation of all — man. And just as the trees, the birds, and all the other works of His hands have a particular function, you have a unique God-given purpose and it is up to you to spend time with the Lord to identify what it is. By doing so, you will not only please God, but you will also be empowered to live a full, satisfied, and complete life.

Please use the *Prayers and Daily Journal* to complete the following items in your action plan.

DAY 1: ACTION PLAN

1. Pray and thank God for creating you with a specific purpose.
2. Pray and ask God to reveal your specific purpose to you.
3. Whether you feel you are young or older, write down your life dreams in your *Prayers and Daily Journal.* (Ask God to reveal the dreams He placed inside of you.)
4. List 100 of your life goals in your *Prayers and Daily Journal.* Some examples include:
    - Receive a bachelor's degree in accounting
    - Own my own home decorating business
    - Purchase a four bedroom, two bath, ranch-style home
    - Secure investment properties, including apartment complexes and condominiums
    - Write a 200-page autobiography, chronicling my life
    - Travel to each continent
    - Amass a $1 million net worth
    - Have two children and raise them in the nurture and admonition of the Lord
    - Donate over $500,000 to my local church
    - Meet and marry the woman of my dreams and love her as Christ loves the church
5. Think about this question: If all of your financial needs were met in abundance, what

would you enjoy doing everyday, for the rest of your life without getting paid for it and be happy?

6. Scripture meditation: Psalm 139:1-17, Psalm 8:1-9

DAY 1: SELF-ASSESSMENT

This self-assessment is not a test. There are no right or wrong answers. It will help you develop a better understanding of your God-given gifts and talents.

1. I believe God made me for a specific purpose.
   ○ Yes   ○ No

2. I believe I have identified my purpose in life.
   ○ Yes   ○ No

3. I am focused on my personal development.
   ○ Yes   ○ No

4. I have a job or career that I really enjoy.
   ○ Yes   ○ No

5. I am currently working in my life work.
   ○ Yes   ○ No

6. I believe my gifts, talents, and abilities are consistent with my work.
   ○ Yes   ○ No

7. I am fully using my gifts, talents, and abilities in my current vocation.
   ○ Yes   ○ No

8. I feel good about who I am.
   ○ Yes   ○ No

9. I feel good about the direction my life is taking.
   ○ Yes   ○ No

10. I believe that God is pleased with who I am.
   ○ Yes   ○ No

WORKPLACE
WISDOM

PURPOSE

DAY TWO

In Day 2, you will discover how your purpose is intricately and progressively revealed to you by God. Even as a young child, your interests, natural talents, and abilities reflected the greatness God placed inside you before birth. You were elaborately and intricately fashioned in the image of God Almighty and He formed you with a magnificent destiny in mind.

2

The Pathway To Discover Your Purpose – The Formative Years

*P*urpose is revealed incrementally by divine revelation from God. It is a powerful life force that inspires, motivates, and pushes you to achieve your absolute best.

From early childhood to adulthood, there are natural abilities that are evident in a child's interactions with others. Parents, and those in authority over children, are especially called by God to pay particular attention to their talents and gifting as they play a pivotal role in defining the child's life purpose.

From repetitive behaviors to interests, there are underlying characteristics that a parent/guardian/authority figure can look for that will aid in identifying a child's motivational gift and God-given purpose. Parents are charged with supporting the growth of their child's God-given gifting through:

- Observation
- Early childhood training
- Motivational gift
- Education
- Hobbies and interests
- Exposure
- Character and moral development
- Early job assignments
- Early mentoring
- Civic duties and volunteering

By selecting educational and vocational systems that support the child's natural abilities and interests, a parent will not only aid in the maturation of their child's God-given talents, but they will also empower them to walk in God's best for their lives.

DAY 2: ACTION PLAN

FOR PARENTS OR GUARDIANS

1. Spend time before the Lord in prayer and ask Him to reveal things to you about your children that will enable you to help them determine their purpose. (John 16:13)

2. Begin to more carefully observe your child in natural environments, paying particular attention to their behaviors and tendencies at a

Please use the *Prayers and Daily Journal* to complete the following items in your action plan.

heightened level. Write down your observations in your *Prayers and Daily Journal*.

3. Write down your observations, including your child's habits, behaviors, thoughts, and so forth, in your *Prayers and Daily Journal*. Have your child journal as well.

4. Ask your child questions and observe his actions and behaviors to help you narrow down his motivational gift.

5. Have your child share his innermost dreams and desires. Place them in your *Prayers and Daily Journal*. Have your child journal in their *Prayers and Daily Journal* as well.

6. Observe your child's hobbies and interests to gain insight into his natural abilities and talents.

7. Expose your child to a wide array of new experiences and occupations.

8. Demonstrate Christian character qualities and morality before your child.

9. Place your child in an educational environment that will promote his gifts, talents, and abilities.

10. Set aside time alone with your child so that

ADDITIONAL THOUGHTS

you may better understand his interests, thoughts, and goals.

11. Assist your child in finding job shadowing, internships, and part-time work in their areas of interest.

12. Assist your child in seeking excellent mentors.

13. Encourage your child to participate in civic and volunteer activities.

14. Be a person who understands and is committed to the greater good.

For All Others

1. Spend time in prayer and ask the Holy Spirit to reveal things from your childhood that will assist you in identifying your life purpose. (John 14:26) Make notes in your *Prayers and Daily Journal* of the revelations you receive.

2. Take time to reflect upon what you remember being interested in performing while growing up and write it down in your *Prayers and Daily Journal.*

3. Prayerfully think about what you enjoyed most as a child, what you were passionate about, and what excited you the most. Place

this information in your *Prayers and Daily Journal.*

4. Write down your childhood dreams in your *Prayers and Daily Journal.*

5. Reflect upon early work, civic, and volunteer experiences. Think about the ones you enjoyed doing the most and write down what made those opportunities more memorable than others in your *Prayers and Daily Journal.* Note the areas you excelled in.

6. Ask your parents, siblings, other relatives, and close family friends about your behaviors and interests as a child. Write down their observations in your *Prayers and Daily Journal.*

7. Reflect on your education, training, and other experiences to identify your natural gifts and abilities and to determine whether you developed your gifts into talents.

8. As a child, which single occupation did you want to become more than any other and why did you choose it over others? Write that occupation in your *Prayers and Daily Journal* and prayerfully take it before God to see if it is His will for your life if you did not pursue it.

DAY 2: SELF-ASSESSMENT

This self-assessment is not a test. There are no right or wrong answers. It will help you develop a better understanding of your God-given gifts and talents.

1. List five activities you enjoyed spending the majority of your time doing as a child (for example, reading, writing, playing an instrument, etc.).

   1. _____

   2. _____

   3. _____

   4. _____

   5. _____

2. What type of jobs excited you as a youth, and why?

   _____

   _____

   _____

   _____

3. List five of your hobbies and interests.

    1. _____

    2. _____

    3. _____

    4. _____

    5. _____

4. Do you have a mentor in your chosen vocation?
    ○ Yes   ○ No

5. Do you volunteer?
    ○ Yes   ○ No
    a. If so, do you volunteer in your chosen vocation?
        ○ Yes   ○ No

WORKPLACE
WISDOM

PURPOSE

DAY THREE

Day 3 focuses on the importance of determining your ruling passion and allowing it to govern your decisions on educational training, activities, and jobs that you undertake during young adulthood. God placed a ruling passion in you that reflects your innermost being. Uncovering your ruling passion is pivotal in discovering your God-given purpose.

3

Narrowing Your Focus – Young Adulthood

O nce you reach young adulthood, you should have ideally determined your motivational gift and be in pursuit of your life work. This entails entering the work force and pursuing a primary vocation that will evolve into many opportunities. Focusing your career on accomplishing your life work helps you remain single-minded and committed to fulfilling God's purpose for your life.

It is critical that you pursue your life passion which is your ruling or governing desires and convictions. It is God-given and represents a key to discovering your purpose and life work. Your ruling passion reflects the essence of your innermost being and should be used as a guide in deciding the vocational/educational training you may need, the civic activities for which you should become involved, and the types of jobs you should undertake.

ADDITIONAL THOUGHTS

Please use the *Prayers and Daily Journal* to complete the following items in your action plan.

By pursuing your life passion, you allow yourself to discover your life purpose and begin to sit in the seat of your life work. Your life work is the work to which you dedicate yourself and achieve your greatest accomplishments. It is reflective of your God-given purpose, motivational gift, and natural gifts and talents.

DAY 3: ACTION PLAN

1. Pray and ask God to show you how to narrow and mature in your purpose. (James 1:5)
2. Perform the self-assessments for Day 3.
   a. Talents and Abilities
   b. Job Skills
   c. Work Environment
   d. Work Preferences
3. Identify your ruling passion and write it in your *Prayers and Daily Journal.*
4. Pray and ask God to help you identify your life work.
5. Select job assignments that match your talents, skills, and abilities.
6. Identify the type of volunteer activities that will help you further identify your life work and life purpose.
7. Identify and engage mentors who will help you determine your purpose.
8. Develop hobbies that give insight and will allow you to mature in your natural talents and abilities.

DAY 3: SELF-ASSESSMENT

This self-assessment is not a test. There are no right or wrong answers. It will help you develop a better understanding of your God-given gifts and talents.

A Prayer for A Priest

Lord Jesus, you have chosen (Father   ) from among us and sent him out to proclaim your word and to act in your name. For so great a gift to your church I give you praise and thanksgiving. I ask you to fill him with the fire of your love, that his ministry may reveal your presence in the Church. Since he is an earthen vessel, I pray that your power shine through his weakness. In his afflictions let him never be crushed; in his doubts never despair; in temptation never be destroyed; in his persecution never abandoned. Inspire him through prayer to live each day the mystery of your dying and rising. In times of weakness send him your Spirit, and help him to praise your heavenly Father and pray for sinners. By the same Spirit put your word on his lips and love in his heart, to bring good news to the poor and healing to the broken-hearted. And may the gift of Mary your Mother, to the disciple whom you loved, be your gift to every priest. Grant that she, who formed you in her human image, may form him in your divine image, by the power of your Spirit, to the glory of God the Father. Amen.

... MENT

...as developed through
...t considered a God-
...s a learned behavior.
...s will influence what
...cient and competent
...rticular skill. (Devel-
...urpose.)

...es traditionally ac-
...nal training, or on-
...influence individual
...re literally hundreds
...ls that can be devel-
...ivities as:

...nry
...r writing
...ekeeping
...g
...tion
...eographing plays
...scaping
...bing
...g books/films

• Cooking

• Playing a musical instrument

- Playing a sport
- Preparing legal documents
- Teaching
- Designing graphic art
- Pet grooming and sitting
- Engineering
- Software programming

- Drawing
- Building homes
- Repairing computers
- Painting
- Public speaking
- Dispensing medicine
- Carpentry

One of the fundamental reasons people are unhappy with their jobs and careers is because of the disparity between the job skills they use at work and the individual's talents that lie dormant. The divide makes job skills performed daily seem routine and mundane.

The selection and mastery of job skills is one of the key indicators of job satisfaction and financial success. Highly successful and developed individuals have effectively identified and developed the job skills which are suitable to their God-given makeup. The development of job skills that are consistent with your purpose is fundamental for success.

List the 20 job skills you are developing or have developed, rate your skill level for that particular function and state whether that job skill is in line with your God-given purpose.

Rating:
    A. master – extremely developed
    B. very developed
    C. somewhat developed
    D. slightly developed
    E. not very developed

Narrowing Your Purpose — Young Adulthood

No.	Job Skill	Rating (A,B,C, D, or E)	I use my God-given talent (y/n)
1			
2			
3			
4			
5			
6			
7			
8			
9			
10			
11			
12			
13			
14			
15			
16			
17			
18			
19			
20			

List 3 of the above job skills that you want to master in the next 2 years and what you need to do in order to master it.

1. _____

_____

2. _____

_____

3. _____

_____

List 5 of the new job skills that are consistent with your natural talents and skills that you would like to develop in the next 2 years.

1. _____

_____

2. _____

_____

3. _____

_____

4. _____

_____

5. _____

_____

TALENTS AND NATURAL ABILITIES

Natural ability is the physical or mental power or capability necessary to accomplish something. Natural ability comes easily to the individual with minimal effort.

There are thousands of natural abilities. Listed below are some of the most commonly identified natural abilities.

Rate your skill level for each of the abilities listed below. Add your ability if it is not listed, and rate yourself.

1. little or no ability
2. slight ability
3. average ability
4. above average ability
5. comes naturally, exceptional ability

Natural Ability	1	2	3	4	5
Athletic ability					
Musical ability					
Physical strength					
Public speaking					
Artistic ability					
Intellectual ability					
Problem solving					
Handling complex situations					
Teaching ability					
Writing ability					
Leadership					
Communication ability					
Presentation skills					
Dealing with stressful situations					
Generating new ideas/inventions					
Working on teams					
Delegating tasks					
Organizing people/objects					
Fixing things					
Hand/eye coordination					
Building new relationships					
Working with people of diverse backgrounds/ethnicities					
Making people feel at ease in uncomfortable situations					

Narrowing Your Purpose — Young Adulthood

List 7 of your top natural abilities.

1. _____

2. _____

3. _____

4. _____

5. _____

6. _____

7. _____

ADDITIONAL THOUGHTS

WORK ENVIRONMENT

What are your ideal work conditions? Do you enjoy working (with)…

Condition	Y	N
Machinery or devices		
Numbers or mathematical calculations		
Theories, ideas, and principles		
Your hands		
Your mind		
Adults		
Children		
By yourself		
Animals		
Outdoors		
Indoors		
Slow-paced		
Moderately paced		
Fast-paced		
Computers/typewriters		
With sounds, such as music		
In a residential setting		
In an office setting		
Structured environment (everything is managed/judged according to a specific policy/procedure)		
Unstructured environment (more relaxed, rules are stated but not always enforced)		

WORK PREFERENCES

What are your preferred work preferences? If you had the ideal job, what type of skills/duties would you enjoy performing?

Preference	Y	N
Presenting information		
Teamwork		
Selling products		
Playing sports		
Musical performance		
Writing procedures/employee protocol/handbooks/etc.		
Ensuring a department/company adheres to environmental, federal, state, and local regulations		
Budget analysis		
Forecasting spending/market trends/product cycles		
Analyzing customer demographics		
Developing company media kits: brochures, pamphlets, fliers, business cards, etc.		
Designing software		
Creating an e-commerce site		
Typing/filing/answering phones		
Data entry		
Employing foreign language skills through interpretation, speaking, and/or writing another language		
Traveling		
Leading a team		
Developing new ideas/products/processes		

PURPOSE

DAY FOUR

Day 4 is the day of breakthrough! It reveals many of the obstacles that may arise along your pathway to purpose. There are countless reasons why you may get diverted, distracted, or thwarted from your pathway to purpose. Day 4 helps you locate yourself, make the necessary adjustments, and begin operating in your purpose.

4

Obstacles
on the Pathway
to Purpose

*M*any of us have faced various obstacles along our pathway to purpose, including:

- Unstable family relationships
- Incest and sexual abuse
- Death
- Controlling and manipulative parents or guardians
- Disinterested teachers and counselors
- Poor mentors
- Religious tolerance — witchcraft
- Unproductive work environments & relationships
- Ungodly relationships

JAMES 4:7 (AMP)
So be subject to God. Resist the devil [stand firm against him], and he will flee from you.

1 PETER 5:8-10 (AMP)
Be well balanced (temperate, sober of mind), be vigilant and cautious at all times; for that enemy of yours, the devil, roams around like a lion roaring [in fierce hunger], seeking someone to seize upon and devour. Withstand him; be firm in faith [against his onset — rooted, established, strong, immovable, and determined], knowing that the same (identical) sufferings are appointed to your brotherhood (the whole body of Christians) throughout the world. And after you have suffered a little while, the God of all grace [Who imparts all blessing and favor], *continued on p. 29...*

- Substance abuse, drug abuse, and other destructive habits
- Financial stress and poor money management
- Tragic events
- Lack of godly character

WE ARE MORE THAN CONQUERORS

It is important to know that:

1. God loves you despite your past and will bless your life once you commit to Him. Despite of the obstacles you were confronted with, there are ways to combat and deal with the issues in order to have victory.

2. Everyone, irrespective of their wealth, fame, and worldly success, is challenged by various stumbling blocks and sometimes finds themselves knocked off their path to purpose.

3. Those who are successful dust themselves off and get back on their path and fulfill their God-given destiny.

4. The prescription is to identify the problems.

5. You need to begin to take the appropriate steps to rectify and resolve the issues.

6. You must have a revelation in your heart that God's grace is sufficient to deal with any problem that may arise in your life.

7. You should not let any obstacle or one of life's challenges deter you from fulfilling your life purpose. God has called you to do great and mighty things on earth, and He is depending on you to fulfill His will for your life.

8. You are an overcomer! And God expects you to maintain the victory that He has wrought over the enemy by applying His Word and resisting the enemy's traps. (John 16:33, 1 John 5:4-5, Romans 8:37)

DAY 4: ACTION PLAN

As you fulfill God's will concerning your life, you must stay on your pathway to purpose and overcome any obstacles that would attempt to hinder you. You would be well guided to complete the following steps.

1. Give your life to the Lord or rededicate yourself back to Him. If you have already done this, consecrate yourself to the Lord to have Him help you.
2. Forgive others for the injustices that they may have done against you — intentionally and/or unintentionally.
3. Spend time in prayer to get God's will and wisdom on how to handle situations.
4. Find out what God's Word has to say about the matter and make a decision to begin to apply His principles immediately.
5. Stop destructive habits and no longer make

...continued from p. 28
Who has called you to His [own] eternal glory in Christ Jesus, will Himself complete and make you what you ought to be, establish and ground you securely, and strengthen, and settle you.

MARK 11:23 (NKJV)
For assuredly, I say to you, whoever says to this mountain, "Be removed and be cast into the sea," and does not doubt in his heart, but believes that those things he says will be done, he will have whatever he says.

Please use the *Prayers and Daily Journal* to complete the following items in your action plan.

PHILIPPIANS 3:13-14 (NKJV)

Brethren, I do not count myself to have apprehended; but one thing I do, forgetting those things which are behind and reaching forward to those things which are ahead, I press toward the goal for the prize of the upward call of God in Christ Jesus.

2 CORINTHIANS 12:9 (NKJV)

And He said to me, "My grace is sufficient for you, for My strength is made perfect in weakness." Therefore most gladly I will rather boast in my infirmities, that the power of Christ may rest upon me.

excuses for neglecting what you know you should be doing. Be led by the Spirit of God and wholeheartedly seek to do His will.

6. Remove yourself from any ungodly situations. Refrain from getting involved in activities that tempt you to engage in and distract you from doing God's will.

7. Get out of ungodly relationships. Begin to surround yourself with godly influences. Get involved in your local church.

8. Refrain from meditating or thinking about negative events of the past. Move on. Once you accept Jesus Christ into your heart as your Lord and Savior, you are a new creation. (2 Cor. 5:17)

9. If you miss the mark in any area and find yourself off your pathway, repent and immediately get back on track. Remember, no matter how many times you miss it, God loves you and is always ready and willing to forgive you. He wants to see you victorious in every situation. (1 John 1:9)

10. If you find yourself off your path to purpose, redirect yourself on to the right road:
    a. Repent for the mistake
    b. Get God's Word on the situation and immediately apply His principles
    c. Forgive yourself and all others involved
    d. Find an excellent mentor
    e. Acquire the appropriate education and job training needed to fulfill your purpose

f. Read books, trade journals and manuals which provide the information that you need

DAY 4: SELF-ASSESSMENT

This self-assessment is not a test. There are no right or wrong answers. It will help you develop a better understanding of your God-given gifts and talents.

What obstacles attempted to prevent you from finding and staying on your Pathway to Purpose?

1. Unstable family relationships
   a. Divorce
      ○ Yes   ○ No

   b. Incest or sexual abuse
      ○ Yes   ○ No

   c. Verbal or physical abuse
      ○ Yes   ○ No

   d. One parent household
      ○ Yes   ○ No

   e. Orphan
      ○ Yes   ○ No

   f. Sibling rivalry
      ○ Yes   ○ No

JOHN 16:33 (AMP)
I have told you these things, so that in Me you may have [perfect] peace and confidence. In the world you have tribulation and trials and distress and frustration; but be of good cheer [take courage; be confident, certain, undaunted]! For I have overcome the world. [I have deprived it of power to harm you and have conquered it for you.]

1 JOHN 5:4-5 (AMP)
For whatever is born of God is victorious over the world; and this is the victory that conquers the world, even our faith. Who is it that is victorious over [that conquers] the world but he who believes that Jesus is the Son of God [who adheres to, trusts in, and relies on that fact]?

ROMANS 8:37 (NKJV)
Yet in all these things we are more than con- querors through Him who loved us.

2 CORINTHIANS 5:17 (NKJV)
Therefore, if anyone is in Christ, he is a new cre- ation; old things have passed away; behold, all things have become new.

1 JOHN 1:9 (NKJV)
If we confess our sins, He is faithful and just to forgive us our sins and to cleanse us from all unrighteousness.

g. Sickness and disease in family
○ Yes   ○ No

h. Premature death of family member
○ Yes   ○ No

i. Tragic events in family
○ Yes   ○ No

j. Lack of love and concern
○ Yes   ○ No

k. Controlling and manipulative parents
○ Yes   ○ No

2. Authorities did not help you develop your talents.
a. You were asked or made to be someone who you were not called to be.
○ Yes   ○ No

b. You were intentionally misguided.
○ Yes   ○ No

c. You were told you could not and would not amount to anything.
○ Yes   ○ No

d. Your God-given gift and talents were ig- nored or not recognized.
○ Yes   ○ No

e. You were overlooked.
    ◯ Yes   ◯ No

f. No one took a serious interest in your personal, academic, professional, or social development.
    ◯ Yes   ◯ No

g. Mentors took advantage of you.
    ◯ Yes   ◯ No

3. You were involved in wrong relationships.
    a. Ungodly relationships
        ◯ Yes   ◯ No

    b. Improper/unproductive romantic relationships
        ◯ Yes   ◯ No

    c. Pre-marital sexual relationships
        ◯ Yes   ◯ No

    d. Adulterous relationships
        ◯ Yes   ◯ No

    e. Gang relationships
        ◯ Yes   ◯ No

    f. Other (specify)
        ◯ Yes   ◯ No

ADDITIONAL THOUGHTS

4. You were involved in substance abuse and had destructive habits.
    a. Illegal drugs
        ○ Yes   ○ No

    b. Alcohol
        ○ Yes   ○ No

    c. Co-drug dependency
        ○ Yes   ○ No

    d. Prescription drugs
        ○ Yes   ○ No

    e. Food — Gluttony
        ○ Yes   ○ No

    f. Compulsive shopping
        ○ Yes   ○ No

    g. Overspending
        ○ Yes   ○ No

    h. Lottery/gambling
        ○ Yes   ○ No

5. You demonstrated a lack of godly character.
    a. Immorality
        ○ Yes   ○ No

    b. Laziness
        ○ Yes   ○ No

c. A guilty conscience
   ○ Yes   ○ No

d. Rebellion
   ○ Yes   ○ No

e. Lack of discipline
   ○ Yes   ○ No

f. Procrastination
   ○ Yes   ○ No

g. Pride and arrogance
   ○ Yes   ○ No

h. Emotional instability
   ○ Yes   ○ No

i. Envy
   ○ Yes   ○ No

j. Lack of creativity
   ○ Yes   ○ No

k. Greed
   ○ Yes   ○ No

l. Fear
   ○ Yes   ○ No

m. Lack of sound, moral ethics and integrity
   ○ Yes   ○ No

6. You were negatively affected by financial decisions.
   a. Family never had enough money (borderline poverty)
      ○ Yes   ○ No

   b. Second and third generation welfare recipient
      ○ Yes   ○ No

   c. Divorce and separation
      ○ Yes   ○ No

   d. Family is overloaded with debt
      ○ Yes   ○ No

   e. Compulsive spending
      ○ Yes   ○ No

   f. Lack of financial intelligence
      ○ Yes   ○ No

   g. Poor business decisions
      ○ Yes   ○ No

WORKPLACE
WISDOM

PURPOSE

DAY FIVE

In Day 5, the motivational gifts are introduced and the motivational gift of the Perceiver is discussed. God has called the Perceiver to intercede on the behalf of others and distinguish between right and wrong.

5

God's Unique Motivational Gifts – Introduction / Perceiver

You were created for a specific God-ordained purpose. It is only when you discover your purpose, that true success may be attained. Until you get on your path to purpose, your life has limited significance.

To fulfill your purpose, God has wired you with a unique perspective and viewpoint that determines the framework from which you operate. This wiring, or motivational gift, is from God and determines the vantage point from which you perceive and respond to life. (Romans 12:6-8)

You only have one motivational gift. However, you may exhibit aspects of the other motivational gifts, which are actually learned behaviors.

Identifying your God-given motivational gift enhances your ability to understand different people. Such understanding can improve your relationships with others — your spouse, children, co-workers, and friends.

Fully understanding your motivational gift is a fundamental ingredient to knowing your purpose and an integral key to effectively interacting with others.

The seven God-given motivational gifts are:
- Perceiver — called of God to distinguish between ethical right and wrong.
- Server — called of God to identify the practical needs of others.
- Teacher — called of God to disseminate information.
- Exhorter — called of God to build people up.
- Giver — called of God to meet needs.
- Administrator — called of God to develop systems.
- Compassion — called of God to meet the emotional needs of others.

In Day 5 of *How to Discover Your Purpose in 10 Days*, the Perceiver motivational gift is discussed. We learned that God called Perceivers to intercede on behalf of others. Perceivers are anointed by God to distinguish between ethical right and wrong. They are vital to helping maintain moral and ethical integrity.

DAY 5: PERCEIVER ACTION PLAN

SECTION A

1. Perform the Perceiver self-assessment. (p 47)

2. Attempt to determine if you are a Perceiver motivational gift.
   a. If yes, continue to section B, question 3 and complete the steps. (Skip section C.)
   b. If no, continue to section C, question 12 and complete the steps.
   c. If unsure, continue to complete all sections concerning the remaining motivational gifts (see Days 5-8) and complete all motivational gift self-assessments.

Please use the *Prayers and Daily Journal* to complete the following items in your action plan.

SECTION B

3. If you have successfully determined that you are a Perceiver, congratulations! You have been wired by God to perceive, recognize, and distinguish between right and wrong. That is a blessing! The identification of your motivational gift is very helpful in determining your God-given purpose.

4. Pray and thank God for how He made you; for you have been fearfully and wonderfully

made. God needed you to be this way to fulfill His plans and purposes for your life.

5. Decide to accept yourself as God made you. Many people don't accept the way God made them. They desire to become another motivational gift rather than who God made them to be. That will slow up your process of development.

6. Review the characteristics of the Perceiver motivational gift and begin to observe your motivational gift in operation in your life. Write your observations in your *Prayers and Daily Journal.*
    a. Observe why and how you make decisions.
    b. Observe how you respond to situations.
    c. Observe your thought processes.
    d. Observe your natural interactions with people.
    e. If your behaviors don't line up with the general characteristics, re-evaluate yourself to determine if you need to re-identify your motivational gift.
    Remember: You do not have to perfectly match every characteristic in order to be that motivational gift.

7. Have those closest to you (spouse, parents, children, close friend) confirm your motivational gift.

a. Have those close to you review the characteristics of the Perceiver and confirm whether you line up with them.

    b. Those close to you will have an independent opinion of how you really act.

    c. If you don't line up, start over in the identification process.

8. After confirming your gift, determine your strengths and begin to develop them at a higher level. List your strengths in your *Prayers and Daily Journal.*

    a. Go back and review the abilities, skills, and interests self-assessments and see if there is a pattern in line with your motivational gift.

    b. Have a heightened awareness of things you do well and that come easily for you.

    c. Begin to develop your strengths through mentorship, formal study or training, and/or home study, including tapes and books.

9. Recognize your weaknesses and place them in your *Prayers and Daily Journal.* These are the areas you will want to temper as you mature.

    a. Determine your weaknesses in social interaction and learn to temper or develop in those areas.

    b. Recognize the areas in which you are

ADDITIONAL THOUGHTS

not naturally gifted and determine how to delegate and defer to others for help.

10. Begin to identify job and work situations in which your motivational gift can be fully expressed.
    a. You may already be in the best situation to express your motivational gift.
    b. You may need to see your present job from a different perspective.
    c. It may mean slightly adjusting your present job responsibilities and duties.
    d. You may need to believe God to be reassigned to a new position in the company or to find a new job. If this is the case, be patient and allow God to direct your steps.

11. Begin to allow your gift to be expressed in your service to other people.
    a. Serve God and the body of Christ in areas that are supported by your motivational gift.
    b. Serve your family, friends, and community, and perform civic duties using your motivational gift.

SECTION C
If you do not possess the motivational gift of Perceiver, consider the following.

12. Identify those in your circle of family and friends who possess this motivational gift.

_____

_____

_____

_____

_____

_____

_____

13. Study the differences in patterns and behavior between the Perceiver and yourself.
    a. The ability to understand others and effectively interact with people is a fundamental key to success.
    b. Think about times you could have misunderstood a Perceiver because you did not understand the gift.
    c. Purpose to attempt to understand the Perceiver rather than judging them.
    d. Learn to accept and not reject the perspective of the Perceiver even though it is different from your own.

e. Pray and ask God to give you wisdom on how to properly interact with the Perceiver motivational gift.

14. Study the strong characteristics of the Perceiver motivational gift and build these characteristics into your behavior patterns.
   a. Learn the positive behaviors of the Perceiver.
   b. Avoid the negative behaviors of the Perceiver.

15. Determine ways to utilize or rely on a Perceiver to help you accomplish your goals and tasks.
   a. Determine the ways someone of this motivational gift can help compensate for your weaknesses.
   b. Determine if you should completely delegate a task to the Perceiver or just ask for advice or help.
   c. Learn to embrace each motivational gift for the unique wisdom and perspective toward life that God gave them.

DAY 5: PERCEIVER MOTIVATIONAL GIFT SELF-ASSESSMENT

	Characteristics of the Perceiver	0	1	2	3	POINTS
1	Not a people person					
2	On Sunday after church (personal time) prefers to be alone or with a very small group					
3	Views moral and ethical issues as black or white with no shades of gray					
4	Quickly and accurately identifies ethical right and wrong					
5	Is considered forthright, outspoken, and blunt					
6	Feels correct all the time					
7	Excellent judge of character					
8	Hard to satisfy, difficult to please					
9	Can be very critical and judgmental					
10	Has difficulty giving encouragement for partial progress					
11	Does not draw energy from people					
12	Considered a loner					
13	Enjoys being alone					
14	Has a small circle of friends					
Key: 0 = Never, 1 = Occasionally, 2 = Often, 3 = Always						

continued on p. 48...

...*continued from p. 47*

ᴀᴅᴅɪᴛɪᴏɴᴀʟ ᴛʜᴏᴜɢʜᴛꜱ

Characteristics of the Perceiver	0	1	2	3	POINTS
15 Views everything as either right or wrong with no in between					
16 Has a strong moral constitution					
17 Has a strong distaste or hatred for wrong					
18 Very alert to dishonesty					
19 Does not like when people lie					
20 Feels obligated to expose wrong					
21 Has strong opinions with strong convictions					
22 Forms opinions instanteously					
23 Has difficulty beating around the bush					
24 Rarely feels wrong					
25 Judges right and wrong very quickly					
26 Thinks independently of others					
27 Will not follow the crowd in making decisions					
28 Extremely hard to influence opinions or feelings once they have been made					
29 As a child would quickly tattle tale on someone who did something wrong					
30 Believes that people should not compromise					
Key: 0 = Never, 1 = Occasionally, 2 = Often, 3 = Always					

continued on p. 49...

...continued from p. 48

Characteristics of the Perceiver	0	1	2	3	POINTS
31 Enjoys getting involved in morally or ethically correct causes					
32 A champion or spokesperson for causes (e.g. abortion, civil rights, political or social causes, etc.)					
33 Implements rules, policies, and guidelines very well					
34 Feels that rules and policies must be obeyed					
35 Makes decisions easily					
36 Can easily sense when someone or something is not what it appears to be					
37 Considers and evaluates what people say and do					
38 Easily identifies faults and shortcomings in others					
39 Often communicates faults without being asked					
40 Views difficulties as opportunities for growth rather than problems					
41 Has very high standards					
42 Demonstrates high levels of integrity and honesty					
43 Can become easily frustrated when things are not done correctly					
44 Feels that principles must be upheld					
Key: 0 = Never, 1 = Occasionally, 2 = Often, 3 = Always					

continued on p. 50...

...continued from p. 49

ADDITIONAL THOUGHTS

Characteristics of the Perceiver	0	1	2	3	POINTS
45	Enjoys being alone and working independently					
46	Feels very comfortable not having continuous people contact					
47	Usually does not give praise or credit unless the task is performed very well					
48	Often does not accept the beliefs and opinions of others					
49	Can be uncompromising and forceful when attempting to get others to develop					
50	Can be critical and judgmental of self					
	Total Points					
Key: 0 = Never, 1 = Occasionally, 2 = Often, 3 = Always						

WORKPLACE
WISDOM

PURPOSE

DAY SIX

In Day 6, the motivational gifts of Server and Teacher are revealed. God has called the Server to perform the practical needs of others, while the Teacher has been anointed by God to manage and disseminate information.

6

God's Unique Motivational Gifts – Server / Teacher

God called Servers to meet the practical needs of others. He called Teachers to manage and disseminate information. In Day 6 of *How to Discover Your Purpose in 10 Days*, the Server and Teacher motivational gifts are discussed in detail.

SERVER

God anointed Servers with a built-in radar to sense what others need. They are very people oriented and enjoy physical activity. Because they derive their greatest satisfaction in life from serving others, they like to multitask and tend to get overloaded. Servers are loyal, enthusiastic, and hardworking. Their purpose is centered around ministering and serving the needs of others.

ADDITIONAL THOUGHTS

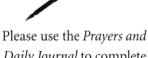

Please use the *Prayers and Daily Journal* to complete the following items in your action plan.

TEACHER

Teachers are anointed to share and disseminate information and usually present it in a systematic and organized format. They enjoy reading and complex problem solving. They are long-range thinkers and tend to be more project oriented than people oriented. They are sensitive to information being taken out of context and feel obligated to expose the truth.

DAY 6: SERVER ACTION PLAN

SECTION A

1. Perform the Server self-assessment.

2. Attempt to determine if you are a Server motivational gift.
   a. If yes, continue to section B, question 3 and complete the steps. (Skip section C.)
   b. If no, continue to section C, question 12 and complete the steps.
   c. If unsure, continue to complete all sections concerning the remaining motivational gifts (see Days 5-8) and complete all motivational gift self-assessments.

SECTION B

3. If you have successfully determined that you

are a Server, congratulations! You have been wired by God to perform the practical needs of others. That is a blessing! The identification of your motivational gift is very helpful in determining your God-given purpose.

4. Pray and thank God for how He made you; for you have been fearfully and wonderfully made. God needed you to be this way to fulfill His plans and purposes for your life.

5. Decide to accept yourself as God made you. Many people don't accept the way God made them. They desire to become another motivational gift rather than who God made them to be. That will slow up your process of development.

6. Review the characteristics of the Server motivational gift and begin to observe your motivational gift in operation in your life. Write your observations in your *Prayers and Daily Journal.*
   a. Observe why and how you make decisions.
   b. Observe how you respond to situations.
   c. Observe your thought processes.
   d. Observe your natural interactions with people.
   e. If your behaviors don't line up with the general characteristics, re-evaluate

ADDITIONAL THOUGHTS

yourself to determine if you need to re-identify your motivational gift.
Remember: You do not have to perfectly match every characteristic in order to be that motivational gift.

7. Have those closest to you (spouse, parents, children, close friend) confirm your motivational gift.
    a. Have those close to you review the characteristics of the Server and confirm whether you line up with them.
    b. Those close to you will have an independent opinion of how you really act.
    c. If you don't line up, start over in the identification process.

8. After confirming your gift, determine your strengths and begin to develop them at a higher level. List your strengths in your *Prayers and Daily Journal*.
    a. Go back and review the abilities, skills, and interests self-assessments and see if there is a pattern in line with your motivational gift.
    b. Have a heightened awareness of things you do well and that come easily for you.
    c. Begin to develop your strengths through mentorship, formal study or training, and/or home study, including tapes and books.

9. Recognize your weaknesses and place them in your *Prayers and Daily Journal.* These are the areas you will want to temper as you mature.

    a. Determine your weaknesses in social interaction and learn to temper or develop in those areas.

    b. Recognize the areas in which you are not naturally gifted and determine how to delegate and defer to others for help.

10. Begin to identify job and work situations in which your motivational gift can be fully expressed.

    a. You may already be in the best situation to express your motivational gift.

    b. You may need to see your present job from a different perspective.

    c. It may mean slightly adjusting your present job responsibilities and duties.

    d. You may need to believe God to be reassigned to a new position in the company or to find a new job. If this is the case, be patient and allow God to direct your steps.

11. Begin to allow your gift to be expressed in your service to other people.

    a. Serve God and the body of Christ in areas that are supported by your motivational gift.

b. Serve your family, friends, and community, and perform civic duties using your motivational gift.

SECTION C
If you do not possess the motivational gift of Server, consider the following.

12. Identify those in your circle of family and friends who possess this motivational gift.

_____

_____

_____

_____

_____

_____

13. Study the differences in patterns and behavior between the Server and yourself.
    a. The ability to understand others and effectively interact with people is a fundamental key to success.
    b. Think about times you could have mis-

understood a Server because you did not understand the gift.

c. Purpose to attempt to understand the Server rather than judging them.

d. Learn to accept and not reject the perspective of the Server even though it is different from your own.

e. Pray and ask God to give you wisdom on how to properly interact with the Server motivational gift.

14. Study the strong characteristics of the Server motivational gift and build these characteristics into your behavior patterns.

a. Learn the positive behaviors of the Server.

b. Avoid the negative behaviors of the Server.

15. Determine ways to utilize or rely on a Server to help you accomplish your goals and tasks.

a. Determine the ways someone of this motivational gift can help compensate for your weaknesses.

b. Determine if you should completely delegate a task to the Server or just ask for advice or help.

c. Learn to embrace each motivational gift for the unique wisdom and perspective toward life that God gave them.

ADDITIONAL THOUGHTS

DAY 6: SERVER MOTIVATIONAL GIFT SELF-ASSESSMENT

	Characteristics of a Server	0	1	2	3	POINTS
1	Is a people person					
2	On Sunday after church (personal time) prefers to be around people					
3	Views moral and ethical issues in shades of gray					
4	Has built in radar for meeting the practical needs of others					
5	Really enjoys helping and assisting others					
6	Has difficulty saying no when someone asks for help					
7	Has tremendous endurance; will stay up all night to help if necessary					
8	Has one speed: fast forward					
9	Loves running errands					
10	Will usually help clean up after parties or events					
11	Loves being around people					
12	Does not see moral issues in black and white					
13	Quickly identifies others practical needs					
14	Will feel disappointed when not allowed to help					
Key: 0 = Never, 1 = Occasionally, 2 = Often, 3 = Always						

continued on p. 61...

...continued from p. 60

Characteristics of a Server	0	1	2	3	POINTS
15 Will meet the needs of others at the expense of their own needs					
16 Will assist others ahead of own family					
17 Will help others and neglect personal responsibilities					
18 Tends to get overloaded and over-involved					
19 Will promise to help more than is physically possible					
20 Has a personal disregard for weariness					
21 Needs less sleep than the average individual					
22 Has a high energy level					
23 Likes to accomplish things quickly					
24 Enjoys physical activity and manual projects more than mental activity					
25 Prefers working with hands					
26 Enjoys shopping					
27 Prefers short-range projects to long-range projects					
28 Prefers focusing on the here and now rather than long term futures					
29 Prefers to do multiple tasks simultaneously					
Key: 0 = Never, 1 = Occasionally, 2 = Often, 3 = Always					

continued on p. 62...

...continued from p. 61

ADDITIONAL THOUGHTS

Characteristics of a Server	0	1	2	3	POINTS
30 Enjoys doing more than one thing at a time					
31 Gets bored when there is not enough to do					
32 Does not like to sit still; has to be doing something					
33 Enjoys displaying hospitality					
34 Loves to entertain people					
35 Loves to give and host parties					
36 Sensitive to the desires, likes, and dislikes of people					
37 Easily remembers others' favorite foods, hobbies, and interests					
38 Very enthusiastic and a positive attitude					
39 Loves to talk					
40 Loves to laugh and smile					
41 Needs to feel appreciated					
42 Prefers not to be in leadership positions					
43 Prefers doing the job rather than delegating it to someone else					
44 Very faithful and helpful to leaders					
45 Prefers not to work alone					
46 May sacrifice quality for speed					
Key: 0 = Never, 1 = Occasionally, 2 = Often, 3 = Always					

continued on p. 63...

...continued from p. 62

Characteristics of a Server	0	1	2	3	POINTS
47 Has difficulty managing priorities					
48 Sometimes considered a workaholic					
49 Is easily hurt when unappreciated					
50 Can become easily distracted					
Total Points					
Key: 0 = Never, 1 = Occasionally, 2 = Often, 3 = Always					

DAY 6: TEACHER ACTION PLAN

Please use the *Prayers and Daily Journal* to complete the following items in your action plan.

SECTION A

1. Perform the Teacher self-assessment.

2. Attempt to determine if you are a Teacher motivational gift.
   a. If yes, continue to section B, question 3 and complete the steps. (Skip section C.)
   b. If no, continue to section C, question 12 and complete the steps.
   c. If unsure, continue to complete all sections concerning the remaining motivational gifts (see Days 5-8) and complete all motivational gift self-assessments.

ADDITIONAL THOUGHTS

SECTION B

3. If you have successfully determined that you are a Teacher, congratulations! You have been wired by God to disseminate and manage information. That is a blessing! The identification of your motivational gift is very helpful in determining your God-given purpose.

4. Pray and thank God for how He made you; for you have been fearfully and wonderfully made. God needed you to be this way to fulfill His plans and purposes for your life.

5. Decide to accept yourself as God made you. Many people don't accept the way God made them. They desire to become another motivational gift rather than who God made them to be. That will slow up your process of development.

6. Review the characteristics of the Teacher motivational gift and begin to observe your motivational gift in operation in your life. Write your observations in your *Prayers and Daily Journal.*
    a. Observe why and how you make decisions.
    b. Observe how you respond to situations.
    c. Observe your thought processes.
    d. Observe your natural interactions with people.

e. If your behaviors don't line up with the general characteristics, re-evaluate yourself to determine if you need to re-identify your motivational gift.
Remember: You do not have to perfectly match every characteristic in order to be that motivational gift.

7. Have those closest to you (spouse, parents, children, close friend) confirm your motivational gift.
   a. Have those close to you review the characteristics of the Teacher and confirm whether you line up with them.
   b. Those close to you will have an independent opinion of how you really act.
   c. If you don't line up, start over in the identification process.

8. After confirming your gift, determine your strengths and begin to develop them at a higher level. List your strengths in your *Prayers and Daily Journal.*
   a. Go back and review the abilities, skills, and interests self-assessments and see if there is a pattern in line with your motivational gift.
   b. Have a heightened awareness of things you do well and that come easily for you.
   c. Begin to develop your strengths through mentorship, formal study or training,

and/or home study, including tapes and books.

9. Recognize your weaknesses and place them in your *Prayers and Daily Journal.* These are the areas you will want to temper as you mature.
   a. Determine your weaknesses in social interaction and learn to temper or develop in those areas.
   b. Recognize the areas in which you are not naturally gifted and determine how to delegate and defer to others for help.

10. Begin to identify job and work situations in which your motivational gift can be fully expressed.
    a. You may already be in the best situation to express your motivational gift.
    b. You may need to see your present job from a different perspective.
    c. It may mean slightly adjusting your present job responsibilities and duties.
    d. You may need to believe God to be reassigned to a new position in the company or to find a new job. If this is the case, be patient and allow God to direct your steps.

11. Begin to allow your gift to be expressed in your service to other people.
    a. Serve God and the body of Christ in

areas that are supported by your motivational gift.

b. Serve your family, friends, and community, and perform civic duties using your motivational gift.

SECTION C

If you do not possess the motivational gift of Teacher, consider the following.

12. Identify those in your circle of family and friends who possess this motivational gift.

_____

_____

_____

_____

_____

_____

_____

_____

ADDITIONAL THOUGHTS

13. Study the differences in patterns and behavior between the Teacher and yourself.
    a. The ability to understand others and effectively interact with people is a fundamental key to success.
    b. Think about times you could have misunderstood a Teacher because you did not understand the gift.
    c. Purpose to attempt to understand the Teacher rather than judging them.
    d. Learn to accept and not reject the perspective of the Teacher even though it is different from your own.
    e. Pray and ask God to give you wisdom on how to properly interact with the Teacher motivational gift.

14. Study the strong characteristics of the Teacher motivational gift and build these characteristics into your behavior patterns.
    a. Learn the positive behaviors of the Teacher.
    b. Avoid the negative behaviors of the Teacher.

15. Determine ways to utilize or rely on a Teacher to help you accomplish your goals and tasks.
    a. Determine the ways someone of this motivational gift can help compensate for your weaknesses.

b. Determine if you should completely delegate a task to the Teacher or just ask for advice or help.

c. Learn to embrace each motivational gift for the unique wisdom and perspective toward life that God gave them.

DAY 6: TEACHER MOTIVATIONAL GIFT SELF-ASSESSMENT

	Characteristics of a Teacher	0	1	2	3	POINTS
1	Likes people but does not have to be around people					
2	On Sunday after church (personal time) prefers to be alone with family or reading					
3	Views moral and ethical issues in black and white with some shades of gray					
4	Enjoys studying and doing research					
5	Has an extensive library					
6	Prefers nonfiction to fiction					
7	When searching for a topic in an encyclopedia, will browse through other topics					
8	Enjoys explaining things to others					
9	Usually received good grades in school					
Key: 0 = Never, 1 = Occasionally, 2 = Often, 3 = Always						

continued on p. 70...

...continued from p. 69

	Characteristics of a Teacher	0	1	2	3	POINTS
10	Can be judgmental and critical					
11	Is very sensitive to truth taken out of context					
12	Enjoys learning					
13	Enjoys reading					
14	Loves books					
15	Enjoys watching documentaries					
16	Loves to give information					
17	Presents information in a systematic and organized format					
18	Will explain information in an orderly fashion (1, 2, 3 or A, B, C)					
19	Is considered analytical and intellectually developed					
20	A quick learner					
21	Thinks a lot					
22	Validates information by researching the facts					
23	Becomes upset if information is used improperly or out of context					
24	Feels called to reveal truth					
25	Validates information based on truth					
26	Thinks more objectively than subjectively					
Key: 0 = Never, 1 = Occasionally, 2 = Often, 3 = Always						

continued on p. 71...

...*continued from p. 70*

Characteristics of a Teacher	0	1	2	3	POINTS
27 Thinks based on facts rather than feelings					
28 Views life with indifference or detachment					
29 Enjoys complex problem solving					
30 Very good problem solver					
31 Prefers not to be the initial public contact					
32 Is very self-disciplined					
33 Is emotionally self-controlled					
34 Is a long-range thinker					
35 Works well alone, independently, or in groups					
36 Believes information has the intrinsic power to produce change					
37 Can learn to be an excellent leader					
38 Very good communicator					
39 Very good decision maker					
40 Usually does not give practical application when giving information					
41 Usually gives more information than is asked for or needed					
Key: 0 = Never, 1 = Occasionally, 2 = Often, 3 = Always					

continued on p. 72...

...continued from p. 71

ADDITIONAL THOUGHTS

Characteristics of a Teacher	0	1	2	3	POINTS
42 Gives information even if unsolicited					
43 Can develop a know-it-all attitude					
44 Enjoys debating and discussing issues					
45 Does not freely give praise					
46 Can become easily distracted by new projects and tasks, often leaving old tasks uncompleted					
47 Enjoys multitasking					
48 Has a select circle of friends					
49 Curious and inquisitive					
50 Likes to work with projects, ideas, and concepts					
Total Points					
Key: 0 = Never, 1 = Occasionally, 2 = Often, 3 = Always					

WORKPLACE
WISDOM

PURPOSE

DAY SEVEN

In Day 7, the motivational gifts of Exhorter and Giver are uncovered. God has called the Exhorter to encourage and build people up, while the Giver has been anointed by God to mobilize resources for the aid and benefit of others.

7

God's Unique Motivational Gifts – Exhorter / Giver

God called Exhorters to build up people and encourage them to live up to their true potential. He called Givers to mobilize resources for the aid and benefit of others. In Day 7 of *How to Discover Your Purpose in 10 Days*, the Exhorter and Giver motivational gifts are discussed in detail.

EXHORTER

The Exhorter is anointed by God to give constructive and helpful advice. They are excellent communicators that thrive on explaining how to do things. Exhorters are results-oriented and prefer the practical application of information to the research of information.

ADDITIONAL THOUGHTS

Please use the *Prayers and Daily Journal* to complete the following items in your action plan.

GIVER

The Giver is anointed by God with a natural business aptitude and is gifted in mobilizing resources. They derive great pleasure from giving resources, money, and possessions to worthy causes. Givers are excellent negotiators and tend to only contribute to legitimate needs.

DAY 7: EXHORTER ACTION PLAN

SECTION A

1. Perform the Exhorter self-assessment.

2. Attempt to determine if you are an Exhorter motivational gift.
   a. If yes, continue to section B, question 3 and complete the steps. (Skip section C.)
   b. If no, continue to section C, question 12 and complete the steps.
   c. If unsure, continue to complete all sections concerning the remaining motivational gifts (see Days 5-8) and complete all motivational gift self-assessments.

SECTION B

3. If you have successfully determined that you are an Exhorter, congratulations! You have

been wired by God to encourage and build people up. That is a blessing! The identification of your motivational gift is very helpful in determining your God-given purpose.

4. Pray and thank God for how He made you; for you have been fearfully and wonderfully made. God needed you to be this way to fulfill His plans and purposes for your life.

5. Decide to accept yourself as God made you. Many people don't accept the way God made them. They desire to become another motivational gift rather than who God made them to be. That will slow up your process of development.

6. Review the characteristics of the Exhorter motivational gift and begin to observe your motivational gift in operation in your life. Write your observations in your *Prayers and Daily Journal.*
   a. Observe why and how you make decisions.
   b. Observe how you respond to situations.
   c. Observe your thought processes.
   d. Observe your natural interactions with people.
   e. If your behaviors don't line up with the general characteristics, re-evaluate yourself to determine if you need to re-identify your motivational gift.

ADDITIONAL THOUGHTS

Remember: You do not have to perfectly match every characteristic in order to be that motivational gift.

7. Have those closest to you (spouse, parents, children, close friend) confirm your motivational gift.
    a. Have those close to you review the characteristics of the Exhorter and confirm whether you line up with them.
    b. Those close to you will have an independent opinion of how you really act.
    c. If you don't line up, start over in the identification process.

8. After confirming your gift, determine your strengths and begin to develop them at a higher level. List your strengths in your *Prayers and Daily Journal.*
    a. Go back and review the abilities, skills, and interests self-assessments and see if there is a pattern in line with your motivational gift.
    b. Have a heightened awareness of things you do well and that come easily for you.
    c. Begin to develop your strengths through mentorship, formal study or training, and/or home study, including tapes and books.

9. Recognize your weaknesses and place them in

your *Prayers and Daily Journal.* These are the areas you will want to temper as you mature.

    a. Determine your weaknesses in social interaction and learn to temper or develop in those areas.

    b. Recognize the areas in which you are not naturally gifted and determine how to delegate and defer to others for help.

10. Begin to identify job and work situations in which your motivational gift can be fully expressed.

    a. You may already be in the best situation to express your motivational gift.

    b. You may need to see your present job from a different perspective.

    c. It may mean slightly adjusting your present job responsibilities and duties.

    d. You may need to believe God to be reassigned to a new position in the company or to find a new job. If this is the case, be patient and allow God to direct your steps.

11. Begin to allow your gift to be expressed in your service to other people.

    a. Serve God and the body of Christ in areas that are supported by your motivational gift.

    b. Serve your family, friends, and community, and perform civic duties using your motivational gift.

SECTION C

If you do not possess the motivational gift of Exhorter, consider the following.

12. Identify those in your circle of family and friends who possess this motivational gift.

_____

_____

_____

_____

_____

_____

_____

13. Study the differences in patterns and behavior between the Exhorter and yourself.
    a. The ability to understand others and effectively interact with people is a fundamental key to success.
    b. Think about times you could have misunderstood an Exhorter because you did not understand the gift.

c.   Purpose to attempt to understand the Exhorter rather than judging them.

d.   Learn to accept and not reject the perspective of the Exhorter even though it is different from your own.

e.   Pray and ask God to give you wisdom on how to properly interact with the Exhorter motivational gift.

14.   Study the strong characteristics of the Exhorter motivational gift and build these characteristics into your behavior patterns.

a.   Learn the positive behaviors of the Exhorter.

b.   Avoid the negative behaviors of the Exhorter.

15.   Determine ways to utilize or rely on an Exhorter to help you accomplish your goals and tasks.

a.   Determine the ways someone of this motivational gift can help compensate for your weaknesses.

b.   Determine if you should completely delegate a task to the Exhorter or just ask for advice or help.

c.   Learn to embrace each motivational gift for the unique wisdom and perspective toward life that God gave them.

DAY 7: EXHORTER MOTIVATIONAL GIFT SELF-ASSESSMENT

Characteristics of an Exhorter	0	1	2	3	POINTS
1 Generally considered a people person, but not always					
2 Also enjoys being alone					
3 Views moral and ethical issues in large shades of gray					
4 When a child, often got in trouble for talking too much					
5 Very outspoken and talkative					
6 People often come to you for counseling					
7 People say you give very good advice					
8 Will quit counseling people if advice is not taken seriously					
9 Usually nonjudgmental					
10 Sometimes people view you as selfish or conceited					
11 Wants people to live a satisfying and productive life					
12 Desires others and self to live up to true potential					
13 Prefers to see the good and overlook the bad					
14 Can easily find the positive in negative situations					
Key: 0 = Never, 1 = Occasionally, 2 = Often, 3 = Always					

continued on p. 83...

God's Unique Motivational Gifts – Exhorter / Giver

...continued from p. 82

	Characteristics of an Exhorter	0	1	2	3	POINTS
15	Notices a person's positive attributes before negative ones					
16	Does not see the need to judge or criticize people					
17	Does not hesitate to speak what is on their heart					
18	Excellent communicator					
19	Wonderful storyteller					
20	Good motivator and sales-person					
21	Generally has a positive attitude					
22	Is very optimistic					
23	Often talks aloud while thinking					
24	Likes to verbalize thoughts to hear how they sound					
25	Learns right and wrong by experience rather than research					
26	Wants to see information applied rather than just received for information sake					
27	Believes that the key to success is properly applying information					
28	Enjoys reading how-to books					
29	Enjoys explaining how to do something					
Key: 0 = Never, 1 = Occasionally, 2 = Often, 3 = Always						

continued on p. 84...

...continued from p. 83

Characteristics of an Exhorter	0	1	2	3	POINTS
30 Is action or results driven rather than principle driven					
31 Prefers to implement plans rather than develop and research plans					
32 Very good at giving directions					
33 Enjoys giving advice					
34 Very good at counseling					
35 Makes decisions quickly and easily					
36 Prefers to make decisions and implement them immediately					
37 Very good leadership abilities					
38 Enjoys leading others and being the boss					
39 Prefers not to work in isolation, but can work very well independently					
40 Highly opinionated and outspoken					
41 Enjoys telling people what to do					
42 Was considered bossy as a child					
43 Often gets in trouble for talking without thinking first					
44 May use information and facts incorrectly to justify beliefs or behavior					
Key: 0 = Never, 1 = Occasionally, 2 = Often, 3 = Always					

continued on p. 85...

...continued from p. 84

Characteristics of an Exhorter	0	1	2	3	POINTS
45 Sometimes embellishes or exaggerates to make a point					
46 Sometimes finds it easy to justify improper ethics					
47 Always looks out for number one					
48 Will often look out for themselves and their family before others					
49 Sometimes viewed as selfish					
50 Sometimes thinks too highly of themselves; can be viewed as prideful or arrogant					
Total Points					
Key: 0 = Never, 1 = Occasionally, 2 = Often, 3 = Always					

DAY 7: GIVER ACTION PLAN

SECTION A

1. Perform the Giver self-assessment.

2. Attempt to determine if you are a Giver motivational gift.
   a. If yes, continue to section B, question 3 and complete the steps. (Skip section C.)
   b. If no, continue to section C, question 12 and complete the steps.
   c. If unsure, continue to complete all sections

concerning the remaining motivational gifts (see Days 5-8) and complete all motivational gift self-assessments.

SECTION B

3. If you have successfully determined that you are a Giver, congratulations! You have been wired by God to mobilize resources for the aid and benefit of others. That is a blessing! The identification of your motivational gift is very helpful in determining your God-given purpose.

4. Pray and thank God for how He made you; for you have been fearfully and wonderfully made. God needed you to be this way to fulfill His plans and purposes for your life.

5. Decide to accept yourself as God made you. Many people don't accept the way God made them. They desire to become another motivational gift rather than who God made them to be. That will slow up your process of development.

6. Review the characteristics of the Giver motivational gift and begin to observe your motivational gift in operation in your life. Write your observations in your *Prayers and Daily Journal.*
    a. Observe why and how you make decisions.

b. Observe how you respond to situations.

c. Observe your thought processes.

d. Observe your natural interactions with people.

e. If your behaviors don't line up with the general characteristics, re-evaluate yourself to determine if you need to re-identify your motivational gift. *Remember: You do not have to perfectly match every characteristic in order to be that motivational gift.*

7. Have those closest to you (spouse, parents, children, close friend) confirm your motivational gift.

   a. Have those close to you review the characteristics of the Giver and confirm whether you line up with them.

   b. Those close to you will have an independent opinion of how you really act.

   c. If you don't line up, start over in the identification process.

8. After confirming your gift, determine your strengths and begin to develop them at a higher level. List your strengths in your *Prayers and Daily Journal.*

   a. Go back and review the abilities, skills, and interests self-assessments and see if there is a pattern in line with your motivational gift.

b. Have a heightened awareness of things you do well and that come easily for you.

    c. Begin to develop your strengths through mentorship, formal study or training, and/or home study, including tapes and books.

9. Recognize your weaknesses and place them in your *Prayers and Daily Journal.* These are the areas you will want to temper as you mature.

    a. Determine your weaknesses in social interaction and learn to temper or develop in those areas.

    b. Recognize the areas in which you are not naturally gifted and determine how to delegate and defer to others for help.

10. Begin to identify job and work situations in which your motivational gift can be fully expressed.

    a. You may already be in the best situation to express your motivational gift.

    b. You may need to see your present job from a different perspective.

    c. It may mean slightly adjusting your present job responsibilities and duties.

    d. You may need to believe God to be reassigned to a new position in the company or to find a new job. If this is the case, be patient and allow God to direct your steps.

11. Begin to allow your gift to be expressed in your service to other people.

    a. Serve God and the body of Christ in areas that are supported by your motivational gift.

    b. Serve your family, friends, and community, and perform civic duties using your motivational gift.

SECTION C

If you do not possess the motivational gift of Giver, consider the following.

12. Identify those in your circle of family and friends who possess this motivational gift.

_____

_____

_____

_____

_____

_____

13. Study the differences in patterns and behavior between the Giver and yourself.

   a. The ability to understand others and effectively interact with people is a fundamental key to success.

   b. Think about times you could have misunderstood a Giver because you did not understand the gift.

   c. Purpose to attempt to understand the Giver rather than judging them.

   d. Learn to accept and not reject the perspective of the Giver even though it is different from your own.

   e. Pray and ask God to give you wisdom on how to properly interact with the Giver motivational gift.

14. Study the strong characteristics of the Giver motivational gift and build these characteristics into your behavior patterns.

   a. Learn the positive behaviors of the Giver.

   b. Avoid the negative behaviors of the Giver.

15. Determine ways to utilize or rely on a Giver to help you accomplish your goals and tasks.

   a. Determine the ways someone of this motivational gift can help compensate for your weaknesses.

   b. Determine if you should completely

delegate a task to the Giver or just ask for advice or help.

   c. Learn to embrace each motivational gift for the unique wisdom and perspective toward life that God gave them.

DAY 7: GIVER MOTIVATIONAL GIFT SELF-ASSESSMENT

Characteristics of a Giver	0	1	2	3	POINTS
1 Is very people oriented					
2 On Sunday after church (personal time) prefers spending time with people rather than being alone					
3 Views moral and ethical issues in shades of gray					
4 Enjoys giving resources, money, possessions, time, and energy to others					
5 Is considered a very good fundraiser					
6 Can be very generous					
7 Started saving money as a young child					
8 Natural business aptitude					
9 Started a business as a child or teenager					
10 Enjoys being acquainted with very important people (VIPs)					
Key: 0 = Never, 1 = Occasionally, 2 = Often, 3 = Always					

continued on p. 92...

...*continued from p. 91*

ADDITIONAL THOUGHTS

	Characteristics of a Giver	0	1	2	3	POINTS
11	Is considered very friendly and outgoing					
12	Can and will sometimes justify inappropriate behavior					
13	Enjoys raising money for worthy causes					
14	Very sensitive to the unmet needs of others					
15	Must validate needs before assisting					
16	Will not give unless convinced the need is legitimate					
17	Able to identify needed resources and connect with unmet needs					
18	Enjoys seeing the results of giving					
19	Wants contributed resources to be maximized and utilized effectively					
20	Wants giving to go directly to worthy causes					
21	Feels fulfilled when involved in contributions that cause a work to be completed					
22	One of the first individuals to contribute resources to a project					
23	Enjoys being the catalyst that causes others to contribute resources					
Key: 0 = Never, 1 = Occasionally, 2 = Often, 3 = Always						

continued on p. 93...

...continued from p. 92

	Characteristics of a Giver	0	1	2	3	POINTS
24	When contributing, desires to become part of the programs or projects					
25	Really enjoys getting involved in the decision-making aspects of the projects to which a contribution is made					
26	Often gives more than what is necessary to make sure need is met					
27	Loves to entertain and host affairs					
28	Often involved in hosting or planning fundraisers					
29	Excellent money managers					
30	Rarely wastes or misspends money					
31	Is an excellent negotiator					
32	Often considered a deal maker					
33	Very industrious and hard working					
34	Enjoys starting new businesses					
35	Enjoys leading people					
36	Often name drops					
37	Is not considered naïve or gullible					

Key: 0 = Never, 1 = Occasionally, 2 = Often, 3 = Always

continued on p. 94...

...continued from p. 93

ADDITIONAL THOUGHTS

	Characteristics of a Giver	0	1	2	3	POINTS
38	May attempt to manipulate or control through contributions; can be controlling and manipulating					
39	Sometimes gives with strings attached					
40	Sometimes pressures others to contribute					
41	Can become upset when others don't see or understand the need to contribute resources					
42	Can be offended if contribution is refused					
43	Will attempt to make people or organizations dependent					
44	Often feels important when people are dependent					
45	Wants everyone to follow in giving					
46	May feel the ends justify the means					
47	Can think and work independently					
48	Enjoys networking with important people					
49	Prefers not to be idle or lazy					
50	Can become an excellent visionary					
	Total Points					
	Key: 0 = Never, 1 = Occasionally, 2 = Often, 3 = Always					

WORKPLACE
WISDOM

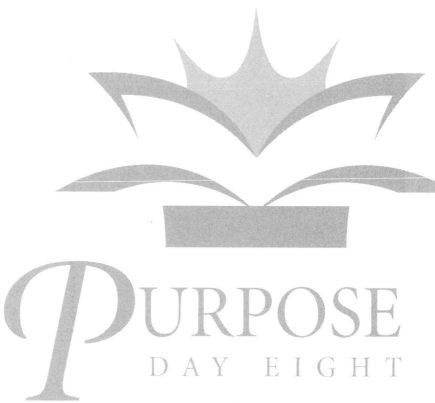

PURPOSE

DAY EIGHT

In Day 8, the motivational gifts of Administrator and Compassion are outlined. God has called the Administrator to facilitate, administrate, and organize, while the Compassion gift is anointed by God to attend to and care for the emotional needs of others. Day 8 also answers the questions and challenges often faced in attempting to narrow down your motivational gift.

8

God's Unique Motivational Gifts – Administrator / Compassion

G od called Administrators to facilitate, organize, and administrate projects and systems. He called the Compassion motivational gift to attend to and care for the emotional needs of others. In Day 8 of *How to Discover Your Purpose in 10 Days*, the Administrator and Compassion motivational gifts are discussed in detail.

ADMINISTRATOR

God has anointed the Administrator to develop and organize effective systems in order to accomplish projects. They are highly skilled at developing and organizing new projects and have tremendous leadership ability. They communicate well and are excellent decision makers.

ADDITIONAL THOUGHTS

Please use the *Prayers and Daily Journal* to complete the following items in your action plan.

COMPASSION

God has anointed the Compassion motivational gift with a keen ability to perceive the emotional needs of others. They are drawn to those in distress. They are very people oriented and derive great pleasure from demonstrating acts of mercy and compassion.

DAY 8: ADMINISTRATOR ACTION PLAN

SECTION A

1. Perform the Administrator self-assessment.

2. Attempt to determine if you are an Administrator motivational gift.
    a. If yes, continue to section B, question 3 and complete the steps. (Skip section C.)
    b. If no, continue to section C, question 12 and complete the steps.
    c. If unsure, continue to complete all sections concerning the remaining motivational gifts (see Days 5-8) and complete all motivational gift self-assessments.

SECTION B

3. If you have successfully determined that you are an Administrator, congratulations! You

have been wired by God to facilitate, organize, and administrate. That is a blessing! The identification of your motivational gift is very helpful in determining your God-given purpose.

4. Pray and thank God for how He made you; for you have been fearfully and wonderfully made. God needed you to be this way to fulfill His plans and purposes for your life.

5. Decide to accept yourself as God made you. Many people don't accept the way God made them. They desire to become another motivational gift rather than who God made them to be. That will slow up your process of development.

6. Review the characteristics of the Administrator motivational gift and begin to observe your motivational gift in operation in your life. Write your observations in your *Prayers and Daily Journal.*
    a. Observe why and how you make decisions.
    b. Observe how you respond to situations.
    c. Observe your thought processes.
    d. Observe your natural interactions with people.
    e. If your behaviors don't line up with the general characteristics, re-evaluate yourself to determine if you need to re-identify your motivational gift.

Remember: You do not have to perfectly match every characteristic in order to be that motivational gift.

7. Have those closest to you (spouse, parents, children, close friend) confirm your motivational gift.
   a. Have those close to you review the characteristics of the Administrator and confirm whether you line up with them.
   b. Those close to you will have an independent opinion of how you really act.
   c. If you don't line up, start over in the identification process.

8. After confirming your gift, determine your strengths and begin to develop them at a higher level. List your strengths in your *Prayers and Daily Journal.*
   a. Go back and review the abilities, skills, and interests self-assessments and see if there is a pattern in line with your motivational gift.
   b. Have a heightened awareness of things you do well and that come easily for you.
   c. Begin to develop your strengths through mentorship, formal study or training, and/or home study, including tapes and books.

9. Recognize your weaknesses and place them in

your *Prayers and Daily Journal.* These are the areas you will want to temper as you mature.

   a. Determine your weaknesses in social interaction and learn to temper or develop in those areas.

   b. Recognize the areas in which you are not naturally gifted and determine how to delegate and defer to others for help.

10. Begin to identify job and work situations in which your motivational gift can be fully expressed.

   a. You may already be in the best situation to express your motivational gift.

   b. You may need to see your present job from a different perspective.

   c. It may mean slightly adjusting your present job responsibilities and duties.

   d. You may need to believe God to be reassigned to a new position in the company or to find a new job. If this is the case, be patient and allow God to direct your steps.

11. Begin to allow your gift to be expressed in your service to other people.

   a. Serve God and the body of Christ in areas that are supported by your motivational gift.

   b. Serve your family, friends, and community, and perform civic duties using your motivational gift.

SECTION C

If you do not possess the motivational gift of Administrator, consider the following.

12. Identify those in your circle of family and friends who possess this motivational gift.

_____

_____

_____

_____

_____

_____

13. Study the differences in patterns and behavior between the Administrator and yourself.
    a. The ability to understand others and effectively interact with people is a fundamental key to success.
    b. Think about times you could have misunderstood an Administrator because you did not understand the gift.
    c. Purpose to attempt to understand the Administrator rather than judging them.

d. Learn to accept and not reject the perspective of the Administrator even though it is different from your own.

    e. Pray and ask God to give you wisdom on how to properly interact with the Administrator motivational gift.

14. Study the strong characteristics of the Administrator motivational gift and build these characteristics into your behavior patterns.

    a. Learn the positive behaviors of the Administrator.

    b. Avoid the negative behaviors of the Administrator.

15. Determine ways to utilize or rely on an Administrator to help you accomplish your goals and tasks.

    a. Determine the ways someone of this motivational gift can help compensate for your weaknesses.

    b. Determine if you should completely delegate a task to the Administrator or just ask for advice or help.

    c. Learn to embrace each motivational gift for the unique wisdom and perspective toward life that God gave them.

DAY 8: ADMINISTRATOR MOTIVATIONAL GIFT SELF-ASSESSMENT

	Characteristics of an Administrator	0	1	2	3	POINTS
1	Not very people oriented					
2	On Sunday after church (personal time) prefers spending time with family or organizing					
3	Views moral and ethical issues in black and white with some shades of gray					
4	Tremendous ability to develop and organize projects					
5	Excellent organizational skills					
6	Very good at developing and organizing effective systems					
7	Natural ability to quickly determine what people do well					
8	Effective delegator					
9	Will assume responsibility, leadership and/or authority when no leadership is clearly defined					
10	Can sometimes view people as projects or resources needed to accomplish the goal					
11	Enjoys organizing					
12	Will organize themselves and others					
Key: 0 = Never, 1 = Occasionally, 2 = Often, 3 = Always						

continued on p. 105...

God's Unique Motivational Gifts — Administrator / Compassion

...continued from p. 104

Characteristics of an Administrator	0	1	2	3	POINTS
13	Very systems oriented					
14	Very detail oriented					
15	Can visualize how people and resources should work together to accomplish a goal					
16	Finds great satisfaction in achieving goals and objectives					
17	Excellent long-range planner					
18	Excellent at project planning					
19	Loves multitasking and variety					
20	Wants to immediately implement the project plan					
21	Desires to see projects completed as quickly as possible					
22	Enjoys starting new projects and will release them once running smoothly					
23	Does not enjoy routine or mundane tasks					
24	Has a clear understanding of how authority functions and operates					
25	Understands, honors, and respects authority					
26	Enjoys being in positions of authority and leadership					
27	Considered a step-in and take-charge individual					
Key: 0 = Never, 1 = Occasionally, 2 = Often, 3 = Always						

continued on p. 106...

...continued from p. 105

Characteristics of an Administrator	0	1	2	3	POINTS
28	If leadership has not been identified or is ineffective, will emerge as the spontaneous leader					
29	Can motivate and organize people to accomplish tasks and goals					
30	Enjoys developing and organizing new projects and challenges					
31	Enjoys distributing tasks and duties					
32	Loves telling others what to do					
33	Delegates very well and will hold others accountable for delegated tasks					
34	Enjoys supervising people					
35	Has the natural ability to keep track of assignments given to others					
36	More project oriented than people oriented					
37	Excellent decision maker					
38	Enjoys using charts, graphs, tables, diagrams, and flowcharts to communicate ideas					
39	Is a visionary that can see long-term benefits and implications					
40	Sometimes considered too bossy					
41	Can be very controlling					
Key: 0 = Never, 1 = Occasionally, 2 = Often, 3 = Always					

continued on p. 107...

...continued from p. 106

Characteristics of an Administrator	0	1	2	3	POINTS
42 Will use people as pawns to accomplish goals					
43 Can be considered a worka-holic					
44 Tends to work others and self beyond personal limitations					
45 Will often neglect home re-sponsibilities to accomplish goals and objectives					
46 Home and work life are often out of balance					
47 Has difficulty relaxing and taking vacations					
48 Loves new challenges and projects					
49 Is an excellent note taker					
50 Very hard worker					
Total Points					
Key: 0 = Never, 1 = Occasionally, 2 = Often, 3 = Always					

DAY 8: COMPASSION ACTION PLAN

SECTION A

1. Perform the Compassion motivational gift self-assessment.

ADDITIONAL THOUGHTS

2. Attempt to determine if you are a Compassion motivational gift.
    a. If yes, continue to section B, question 3 and complete the steps. (Skip section C.)
    b. If no, continue to section C, question 12 and complete the steps.
    c. If unsure, continue to complete all sections concerning the remaining motivational gifts (see Days 5-8) and complete all motivational gift self-assessments.

SECTION B

3. If you have successfully determined that you are a Compassion motivational gift, congratulations! You have been wired by God to attend to and care for the emotional needs of others. That is a blessing! The identification of your motivational gift is very helpful in determining your God-given purpose.

4. Pray and thank God for how He made you; for you have been fearfully and wonderfully made. God needed you to be this way to fulfill His plans and purposes for your life.

5. Decide to accept yourself as God made you. Many people don't accept the way God made them. They desire to become another motivational gift rather than who God made them to be. That will slow up your process of development.

6. Review the characteristics of the Compassion motivational gift and begin to observe your motivational gift in operation in your life. Write your observations in your *Prayers and Daily Journal.*

    a. Observe why and how you make decisions.
    b. Observe how you respond to situations.
    c. Observe your thought processes.
    d. Observe your natural interactions with people.
    e. If your behaviors don't line up with the general characteristics, re-evaluate yourself to determine if you need to re-identify your motivational gift.
    Remember: You do not have to perfectly match every characteristic in order to be that motivational gift.

7. Have those closest to you (spouse, parents, children, close friend) confirm your motivational gift.

    a. Have those close to you review the characteristics of the Compassion motivational gift and confirm whether you line up with them.
    b. Those close to you will have an independent opinion of how you really act.
    c. If you don't line up, start over in the identification process.

8. After confirming your gift, determine your

strengths and begin to develop them at a higher level. List your strengths in your *Prayers and Daily Journal*.

   a. Go back and review the abilities, skills, and interests self-assessments and see if there is a pattern in line with your motivational gift.

   b. Have a heightened awareness of things you do well and that come easily for you.

   c. Begin to develop your strengths through mentorship, formal study or training, and/or home study, including tapes and books.

9. Recognize your weaknesses and place them in your *Prayers and Daily Journal*. These are the areas you will want to temper as you mature.

   a. Determine your weaknesses in social interaction and learn to temper or develop in those areas.

   b. Recognize the areas in which you are not naturally gifted and determine how to delegate and defer to others for help.

10. Begin to identify job and work situations in which your motivational gift can be fully expressed.

   a. You may already be in the best situation to express your motivational gift.

b. You may need to see your present job from a different perspective.

c. It may mean slightly adjusting your present job responsibilities and duties.

d. You may need to believe God to be re-assigned to a new position in the company or to find a new job. If this is the case, be patient and allow God to direct your steps.

11. Begin to allow your gift to be expressed in your service to other people.

    a. Serve God and the body of Christ in areas that are supported by your motivational gift.

    b. Serve your family, friends, and community, and perform civic duties using your motivational gift.

SECTION C

If you do not possess the motivational gift of Compassion, consider the following.

12. Identify those in your circle of family and friends who possess this motivational gift.

_____

_____

_____

_____

_____

_____

_____

_____

13. Study the differences in patterns and behavior between the Compassion motivational gift and yourself.

    a. The ability to understand others and effectively interact with people is a fundamental key to success.

    b. Think about times you could have misunderstood a Compassion motivational gift because you did not understand the gift.

    c. Purpose to attempt to understand the Compassion motivational gift rather than judging them.

    d. Learn to accept and not reject the perspective of the Compassion motivational gift even though it is different from your own.

    e. Pray and ask God to give you wisdom on how to properly interact with the Compassion motivational gift.

14. Study the strong characteristics of the Compassion motivational gift and build these characteristics into your behavior patterns.

a. Learn the positive behaviors of the Compassion motivational gift.

    b. Avoid the negative behaviors of the Compassion motivational gift.

15. Determine ways to utilize or rely on a Compassion motivational gift to help you accomplish your goals and tasks.

    a. Determine the ways someone of this motivational gift can help compensate for your weaknesses.

    b. Determine if you should completely delegate a task to the Compassion motivational gift or just ask for advice or help.

    c. Learn to embrace each motivational gift for the unique wisdom and perspective toward life that God gave them.

DAY 8: COMPASSION MOTIVATIONAL GIFT SELF-ASSESSMENT

Characteristics of a Compassion	0	1	2	3	POINTS
1 Very people oriented					
2 Loves people, loves being around people					
3 On Sunday after church (personal time) wants to be around people					
4 Views moral and ethical issues in shades of gray					
5 Very perceptive and sensitive to the emotional needs of others					
6 Will often bring home stray dogs, cats, and people					
7 Has a great desire to assist those who are emotionally distressed					
8 Is usually noncritical and nonjudgmental					
9 Does not argue or get involved in controversy					
10 Cries easily					
11 Can easily recognize if people are up or down, elated or blue, calm or worried, content or frustrated					
12 Has an intense ability to identify with what others are experiencing					
Key: 0 = Never, 1 = Occasionally, 2 = Often, 3 = Always					

continued on p. 115...

...*continued from p. 114*

Characteristics of a Compassion	0	1	2	3	POINTS
13 Has extraordinary ability to demonstrate care and concern for others					
14 Has a great ability to exhibit love and compassion for others					
15 Feels drawn to people who are suffering or in distress					
16 Will immediately notice when someone is suffering grief or misery					
17 Wants to help to alleviate the emotional stress and hurts of others					
18 Wants to help the needy and downtrodden					
19 Enjoys demonstrating acts of compassion & mercy					
20 Is known for acts of kindness and compassion					
21 Is grieved when others are overlooked or hurt					
22 Feels bad when others feel bad					
23 Excellent at reading body language					
24 Can easily sense how people are feeling					
25 Enjoys doing thoughtful things for others					
26 Usually regarded as very thoughtful and considerate					
Key: 0 = Never, 1 = Occasionally, 2 = Often, 3 = Always					

continued on p. 116...

...continued from p. 115

Characteristics of a Compassion	0	1	2	3	POINTS
27	Generally considered non-confrontational					
28	Does not handle conflict well					
29	Gets feelings hurt easily					
30	Considered a lover, not a fighter					
31	Wants everybody to be happy					
32	Attempts to establish peace and harmony in most relationships					
33	Becomes upset easily					
34	Considered very emotional					
35	Can be very creative					
36	Relies more on emotions than mental processes to make decisions					
37	Governed by heart rather than head					
38	Very affectionate					
39	Does not like to work alone					
40	Prefers not to be in leadership positions					
41	Prefers to follow rather than lead					
42	Does not like to hurt other people's feelings					
43	Has one tempo or pace: slow forward					
Key: 0 = Never, 1 = Occasionally, 2 = Often, 3 = Always						

continued on p. 117...

...continued from p. 116

Characteristics of a Compassion	0	1	2	3	POINTS
44 Prefers not to be pressured or rushed in a duty or undertaking					
45 Does not like to multitask; prefers to focus on one job or project at a time					
46 Usually considered very truthful and sincere					
47 Struggles with decision making					
48 Makes decisions based on feelings rather than facts or intellect					
49 Often takes things too personally					
50 Can sometimes be too sensitive					
Total Points					
Key: 0 = Never, 1 = Occasionally, 2 = Often, 3 = Always					

WORKPLACE
WISDOM

PURPOSE

DAY NINE

By Day 9, you should have begun to discover your God-given purpose. With this exciting revelation, you will learn how important it is to become more developed and mature in your purpose. It is God's desire that you dominate to His glory in your vocation. To do this, you must mature in your life work. Not only will you please God, you will also live a satisfied and fulfilled life.

9

Maturing in Your Purpose – The Adult Years

*A*dulthood is one of the most exciting times for you to continue to grow and develop in your life purpose. By focusing your time and energy on the activities and opportunities that allow you to utilize your natural talents, skills, and abilities, you further enable yourself to realize your full God-given potential.

The most successful people in life are those who determine their purpose. For some, it happens early in life, typically in their thirties. This includes Jesus, Joseph, and David. However, others do not get into their life purpose until later in life, such as Moses, who began his God-given destiny in his eighties. Yet, it is important to know that God desires to use you and He wholeheartedly wants you to operate in His fullness for your life, no matter what your age. The Bible says that the gifts and calling of God are without repentance. Therefore, do just as Jesus, Joseph, Moses,

ROMANS 11:29 (AMP)
For God's gifts and His call are irrevocable. [He never withdraws them when once they are given, and He does not change His mind about those to whom He gives His grace or to whom He sends His call.]

Please use the *Prayers and Daily Journal* to complete the following items in your action plan.

and countless others have done, and do not allow adverse circumstances to hinder or prevent you from walking in God's best for your life.

Remember, God has especially equipped to do great and mighty things on earth as you fulfill your purpose.

DAY 9: ACTION PLAN

1. Pray and ask the Lord to reveal the areas that you need to mature and become more highly specialized in. Write them in your *Prayers and Daily Journal.*

2. Identify and engage highly developed mentors in your vocational area.

3. Find compatible volunteer activities that will support the growth of your natural talents, gifts, and abilities.

4. Find specific ways to increase your vocational knowledge. Place them in your *Prayers and Daily Journal* for reference. You may:
   a. Take continuing education courses
   b. Read trade journals
   c. Read books
   d. Pursue on-the-job training

5. Identify and make a list in your *Prayers and Daily Journal* of all the hobbies you may be-

come actively involved in that will result in the maturation and development of your abilities and talents.

6. As you mature in your purpose, become a mentor to someone else to help them in their process of development.

7. Get involved in activities that will keep you abreast of technological and industry changes and advances. Involvement may include trade associations or unions. Charities may also provide the opportunity for industry growth.

DAY 9: SELF-ASSESSMENT

This self-assessment is not a test. There are no right or wrong answers. It will help you develop a better understanding of your God-given gifts and talents.

1. Have you identified your ruling passion?
    ○ Yes   ○ No

2. Have you begun to mature in your talents and abilities?
    ○ Yes   ○ No

3. Do you feel as though you have begun to mature in your purpose?
    ○ Yes   ○ No

4. Have you identified seasoned mentors in your field?
    ○ Yes   ○ No

5. Have you identified your motivational gift?
    ○ Yes   ○ No

6. Are you involved in a trade association or union?
    ○ Yes   ○ No

7. Are you involved in volunteerism?
    ○ Yes   ○ No
    a. If yes, is it allowing you to develop in your gifts, talents, and abilities?
        ○ Yes   ○ No

8. Have you identified your strengths and weaknesses?
    ○ Yes   ○ No

9. Do you continually partake in job training and continuing education?
    ○ Yes   ○ No

10. For the highly developed individual, are you known for performing an excellent job?
    ○ Yes   ○ No

11. Name two specific things you are known for performing really, really well.

_____

_____

12. Do people solicit advice from you in your field because of your expertise?

    ○ Yes   ○ No

13. Are you current with the latest technology and industry standards and changes in your area/field?

    ○ Yes   ○ No

WORKPLACE
WISDOM

PURPOSE

DAY TEN

There is a great life work that the Lord is counting on you to fulfill. There is also an awesome destiny that God has prepared before the foundation of the world for you to realize. So, this power-packed series concludes on Day 10 centering on how to make your purpose a reality in your life.

10

Fulfilling the Greatness Within

You have been fearfully and wonderfully made in the image of God Himself. He knew exactly what He was doing when He formed you and fashioned you after Himself. He created you with a purpose — an awesome destiny.

There is greatness locked inside of you and it is only when you begin to operate in your purpose that you will fulfill your destiny.

Your ruling passion that the Lord placed within you yearns for manifestation, and it is God's best that it is expressed through your life work and life service/ministry.

The combination of your life work and life service/ministry equal your life purpose. Your life purpose reflects the very essence of your being and it has eternal impact. It has been given to you by God and should be obvious to all who encounter you — defining your life message.

Please use the *Prayers and Daily Journal* to complete the following items in your action plan.

It is vital to discover and operate in your God-ordained purpose. By doing so, your life work, life service/ministry, and life message will reflect the inner greatness God has placed within you.

DAY 10: ACTION PLAN

1. Pray and thank God for creating you with a specific purpose.

2. Write out your life purpose in your *Prayers and Daily Journal.*

3. In your *Prayers and Daily Journal,* state your present life message. Also, state what you want your life message to be in the future.

4. Create and write a vision statement in your *Prayers and Daily Journal* of what God has placed on your heart to accomplish in your lifetime.

5. Prayerfully reflect on how you currently spend your time. Prayerfully reflect on what adjustments need to be made to ensure that your time is being spent most effectively to the glory of God.

6. Seek the Lord's direction on how to move along the continuum of life purpose so that you will get into the stage of Life Purpose Fulfilled.

7. Identify ways you can become highly developed in your purpose and list them in your *Prayers and Daily Journal.*

8. Spend time in prayer and ask the Lord to reveal to you the areas you need to focus on to mature and develop in your purpose. Write them in your *Prayers and Daily Journal.* Work hard to be faithful.

9. Make your decision to be excellent in all areas of your life service, including:
    a. Relationship with God
    b. Family
    c. Church
    d. Workplace
    e. Friends
    f. Community
    g. Civic duty

ADDITIONAL THOUGHTS

DAY 10: SELF-ASSESSMENT

This self-assessment is not a test. There are no right or wrong answers. It will help you develop a better understanding of your God-given gifts and talents.

1. Identify how you currently spend your time versus how you would ideally like to use your time.

   a. Spending time with God

      Current _____%   Ideal _____%

   b. Spending time with your family

      Current _____%   Ideal _____%

   c. Serving in your local church

      Current _____%   Ideal _____%

   d. Working in your vocation

      Current _____%   Ideal _____%

   e. Performing civic duties

      Current _____%   Ideal _____%

   f. Volunteering

      Current _____%   Ideal _____%

2. Do you feel that you have a strong relationship with God?

   ○ Yes   ○ No

3. Do you witness Jesus Christ and His saving power to others?

   ○ Yes   ○ No

4. When you are at work, do you show the love of God in the workplace by doing acts of kindness and compassion?

   ○ Yes   ○ No

5. What stage are you in on the Life Purpose continuum?

   ○ Life Purpose Fulfilled
   ○ Life Purpose Marginally Fulfilled
   ○ Life Purpose Hindered
   ○ Life Purpose Perverted

6. Do you feel like you are an excellent example to others?

   ○ Yes   ○ No

7. Do your hobbies and interests reflect your life purpose?

   ○ Yes   ○ No

8. Have you begun to mature in your life purpose?

   ○ Yes   ○ No

Develop a plan of how to get from where you are today to Life Purpose Fulfilled. Make detailed notes in your *Prayers and Daily Journal.*

9. Is your life message communicating what you desire?

    ○ Yes   ○ No

10. After completing the study of *How to Discover Your Purpose in 10 Days Self-Assessment Workbook,* are you prepared to do what it takes to fulfill your destiny?

    ○ Yes   ○ No

IF YOU DO NOT KNOW THE LORD, GIVE YOUR HEART TO JESUS TODAY

The Word of God says in Romans 10:9-10, that "if you shall confess with your mouth the Lord Jesus, and believe in your heart that God has raised Him from the dead, you will be saved. For with the heart one believes unto righteousness, and with the mouth confession is made unto salvation."

If you do not know the Lord as your Savior, you can recite this simple prayer of salvation: I believe Jesus Christ is the Son of God, that He carried my sins for me, and that He died on the cross at Calvary. He was put in a grave, but I believe He is risen and alive right now. Lord Jesus, come into my heart and save me now. I believe in my heart, therefore I confess with my mouth that Jesus Christ is now my personal Lord and Savior. Thank you Lord for saving me now. In Jesus' name, I pray. Amen.

(If you prayed this prayer, congratulations! We are so very excited for you. We want to e-mail you a free e-book to help you on your Christian journey. Please contact us at info@eaganbooks.com.)

WORKPLACE
WISDOM

Share Your
Personal Testimony
with Us

We would love to hear about the awesome things that the Lord has done in your life as a result of your reading and applying the principles we have shared in this book. Let us know how this book has affected you and what other information you would like us to share in future material at info@eaganbooks.com.

We also invite you to send us your e-mail address, so that we may send you a complimentary copy of The Eagan Report on a periodic basis. For more information, visit our web site: www.eaganbooks.com.

God bless you!

Remember, God is expecting greatness in your life!

Other Resources

If you enjoyed *How to Discover Your Purpose in 10 Days Self-Assesment Workbook*, we also recommend other resources by Dr. J. Victor and Catherine B. Eagan.

DOMINATING MONEY: PERSONAL FINANCIAL INTELLIGENCE
- *Dominating Money, 16-Set Series*
- *10 Keys to Dominating Money, 2-Set Series*
- *Eliminating Debt, 2-Set Series*
- *Budgeting, 2-Set Series*

ADDITIONAL THOUGHTS

ANOINTED FOR WORK: USING THE TOOLS FROM SUNDAY TO SUCCEED ON MONDAY

- *Anointed for Work, 14-Set Series*

DOMINATING BUSINESS: HOW TO PROSPER ON YOUR JOB

- *Dominating Business, 16-Set Series*
- *Servant Leadership, 2-Set Series*
- *What Type of Businessperson Would Jesus Have Been? 2-Set Series*
- *Your Work Matters to God, 2-Set Series*

HOW TO DETERMINE YOUR MOTIVATIONAL GIFT: LEARN HOW GOD WIRED YOU

- *How to Determine Your Motivational Gift, 15-Set Series*

HOW TO DISCOVER YOUR PURPOSE IN 10 DAYS: GOD'S PATH TO A FULL AND SATISFIED LIFE

- *How to Discover Your Purpose in 10 Days, 12-CD Series*
- *How to Discover Your Purpose in 10 Days, 12-DVD Series*

HOME-STUDY COURSES AVAILABLE
- *Dominating Money*
- *Dominating Business*
- *Anointed for Work*

WORKPLACE STUDY MATERIALS
- *Word @ Work, Volume I*
- *Word @ Work, Volume II*

WORKPLACE WISDOM INSTITUTE
www.workplacewisdominstitute.com

What Is the Workplace Wisdom Institute?

Workplace Wisdom Institute is a systematic series of eight, 8-week online courses designed to teach you how to practically apply biblical principles and the Word of God in the workplace. The goal is to encourage the character and excellence of Christ in the workplace. Christians should be the most profitable, highly-successful and fully-satisfied people at work.

Who Should Take These Courses?

These courses are recommended for working people, entrepreneurs, business professionals, managers, supervisors and all people in the workplace from the CEO to every level; and anyone called to practice the principles of God in the workplace, namely every Christian.

ADDITIONAL THOUGHTS

COURSE OFFERINGS

How to Prosper on Your Job

Find out what God's Word says about prospering and increasing on your job.

How to Take God's Power to Your Job

Learn how to be more powerful than your non-Christian counterparts in every situation.

How to Determine Your Motivational Gift

Learn how God wired you and understand why you and others have different views.

Dominating Money — Personal Finance

Areas of focus include budgeting, credit, debt, cash flow, estate planning, and more!

The Character of Success

Increase productivity, profitability, and teamwork to excel to the glory of God.

Godly Leadership and Ethics

Integrate highly successful strategies to maximize the gifts and talents of your team.

Dominating Money — In Business

Learn how to start and manage businesses and the principles of millionaire thinking.

How to Terminate Conflict
Neutralize conflict completely with superiors, co-workers, and others.

How to Discover Your Purpose in 10 Days
Discover your unique, God-given, life assignment so that you may live a full and satisfied life and be in the perfect will of God.

For on-line course information, please visit www.workplacewisdominstitute.com.

WORKPLACE
WISDOM